SEX PLAY

Dedication
To the nicest and sexiest of the Campbell clan.

Acknowledgments
My thanks to Lynn Paula Russell and Monica Guevara
for their splendid, raunchy artwork.

THE *Erotic* Print Society
London 2001

the Erotic Print Society
EPS, 1 Maddox Street
LONDON W1S 2PZ

Tel (UK only): 0800 026 25 24
Fax: +44 (0)207 437 3528
Email: eros@eps.org
Web: www.eroticprints.org

ISBN - 1 - 898998 - 40 - X

Design by Michael Kammerling

THE ART OF LOVE

SEX PLAY

dr david delvin

foreplay techniques for a happy and fulfilled sex life

THE *Erotic* Print Society

CONTENTS

why sex play is important

The first person who wrote a book called *The Art of Love* was the Roman poet Ovid.

He'd been lucky enough to enjoy a great deal of pleasure in the beds and bathtubs of generous-minded Roman maids and matrons.

And in his book (whose Latin title is *Ars Amatoria*), he tried to share some of the sexual knowledge he'd acquired, and to explain how to make sex a delightful experience for both partners.

When the book was published (in the year 1 BC), the authorities promptly reacted by banishing him to a distant province. For life.

Well, let's hope that doesn't happen to me… Meantime, let's do as Ovid did, and look at what sex play, or 'love play', or 'foreplay' (call it what you will) can do for a relationship.

There are lots of benefits of sex play:

- It helps to bring a loving couple closer together.
- It lessens the chances of infidelity– because you're getting so much fun at home.

- For women, it's absolutely essential – because it helps the love juices flow and also encourages the entrance to the vagina to relax and open up.
- It helps women to CLIMAX – and vast numbers of females simply can't reach orgasm without it.
- It helps to give men a good, confident erection.
- It's wonderful fun.

But before we start, a quick word about the terminology of sex play. I've found that a high proportion of couples find it difficult to tell each other what they want in bed, because they don't know the right words or are embarrassed to say them.

I suggest that the two of you go ahead and agree that you're going to use all the frank sex play expressions that you're about to find in this book. Once you get accustomed to it, you'll probably discover that using this explicit talk together is a real turn-on. Also, you'll communicate much, much better.

Sex play becomes very easy if you use the honest, straightforward phrases that you'll find in the next few chapters – and perhaps say:

'Honey, will you frig my clitoris for me?'

or

'Sweetie, will you please touch up my cock?'

In case you're in any doubt, expressions like 'frig', 'touch up', 'rub up', 'wank' and 'masturbate' all mean the same thing: rubbing the genitals with the fingers to produce pleasure and excitement.

You may well have grown up believing that the above words can only mean giving *yourself* sexual pleasure. In fact, this isn't true: you can frig or toss off your partner – and I sincerely hope that you will!

Not that there's anything wrong with doing it to yourself. An interesting development of the last few years has been this: most sexperts have reached the conclusion that it's a very good thing for couples to touch themselves up *in front of each other* as part of sex play.

Why? For three reasons:

1   It shows your partner exactly HOW you like to be touched up.

2   It increases the feeling of intimacy and sharing secret things between a devoted couple.

3   It's often a tremendous turn-on for your partner! It is no accident that sex videos so often feature shots of women masturbating – many males find this sight quite thrilling. And quite a lot of 21st century women enjoy the sight of *men* touching themselves up.

In addition, experts now recognize that self-masturbation during or just before intercourse is often a sensible idea. The reasons for that are pretty obvious:

*   It helps a man get and maintain an erection. Many guys lose their stiffy either just before or during intercourse.
*   It helps the woman to reach her climax.

So, in this book I will be actively urging you to touch yourself up when necessary – just like the lady in the 'Jolly Lovers' illustration (see pages 10 - 11) who is literally lending her husband a hand …

OK. So have fun, and practise safe sex. Turn the page, and in Chapters One and Two you'll discover all about basic anatomy, what to call things – and how the various bits of your body can be turned on by loving, lovely, sex play caresses. Enjoy.

SEX PLAY

a touch
of love

the anatomy of sex play for women

A BASIC GUIDE

Now, this chapter will give you a no-nonsense guide to your bloke's 'naughty bits', showing you the good places to touch – and also the places where you need to take it rather more easily.

If you and your partner have a quick glance through this chapter – and the next one, which is about *female* anatomy – it'll pay you rich dividends.

You will understand far more about your man's sex organs – and your own – than you ever did before. This will help you to give and to receive many really beautiful feelings.

Also, the fact that you both know more about these intimate parts of the human body could well benefit you both *healthwise*.

Why? Well, if you become thoroughly familiar with the appearance and feel of the sex organs in their normal state, then it'll be easier for you to detect if things start going wrong! This is important: far too many people are so vague about their genitals that they don't even realize that something is amiss when a lump or a skin lesion develops.

So, please read this chapter while examining your partner's sexy parts – with warm hands. Get used to inspecting them, handling them, and noting their natural textures and aromas. Enjoy it!

Finally, please note that I'll be using honest, basic, Anglo-Saxon terms for the organs, so that everybody can understand what we're talking about.

YOUR PARTNER'S COCK

Yes, we ARE talking about his penis, prick, John Thomas, pecker (an American expression), tool, male organ, *zizi*, or what you will.

Have a glance at the illustration on the opposite page and you'll see a penis in its rampant glory. Let's look at all the various parts of it, from top to bottom.

ITS HEAD (OR GLANS)

This is about the size of an average plum, and in fact it tends to be quite a rich, plummy sort of colour when it's excited. The head is the bit which nuzzles against your cervix during intercourse. It's also the male equivalent of the tip of your clitoris – so it's pretty sensitive.

In later chapters, we'll explain various ways of stimulating the head with the fingertips and tongue. But for the moment, I'd like to make one brief point about *hygiene*.

Men produce flecks of a white material that tends to collect just below the lower edge of the glans. Doctors think that this stuff isn't awfully hygienic – either for the

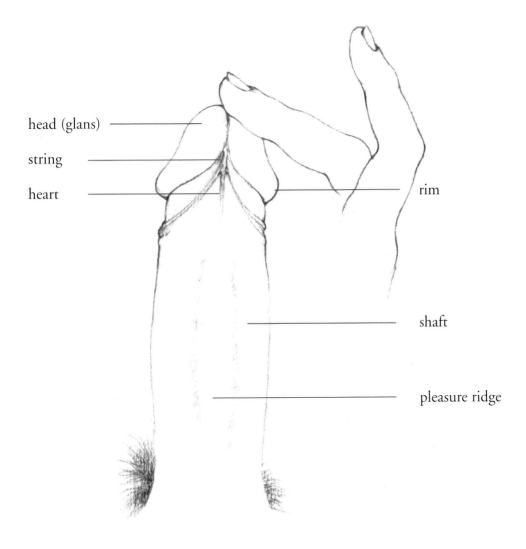

head (glans)

string

heart

rim

shaft

pleasure ridge

his penis

woman OR the man. So it needs to be washed away once a day or so. Don't have any kind of sex with a guy who has this white matter under the head of his cock. Make him go and wash first!

ITS 'HEART'

I christened this bit of the male organ with this name – for the very obvious reason that it looks like an upside-down heart.

If you've got any doubts about where it is, let me make clear that it's on the side of the penis which is FARTHER from the man's belly when he's erect. Incidentally, because long experience has taught me that people get hopelessly confused as to which side of the John Thomas doctors are talking about, I now call this side 'the heart side'. (The other side – the one that is NEARER his tummy when he's erect – I call 'the belly side'.)

The heart of the penis is a wonderful place for you to caress or lick, in ways that I'll detail in Chapters Four and Six. For the moment, let's just say that it's packed full of sensitive nerve-endings that are particularly responsive to the tip of the female tongue.

ITS HEARTSTRING

This is a narrow filament of erotically tuned tissue that runs straight down the middle of the heart to join the shaft of your man's organ. It's either deep pink or black – depending on your guy's skin colour.

As you can see from the illustration on the previous page it is very tightly stretched during erection.

As is often the case with a tightly-stretched string, it's possible to play some really interesting tunes on it! We'll be teaching you how to play, among other things, the famous Butterfly Flick.

ITS FORESKIN (PREPUCE)

You can just see the foreskin in the illustration on page 18 which shows the non-erect willy. It's a little frill of skin that comes down over the head of the penis. It shouldn't be visible when your man is erect, because it's supposed to slide back – thus allowing his cock to lengthen substantially. In a minority of males, it *doesn't* go back properly during erection, and that means that it is too tight. So if the head of your guy's prick is still covered by his foreskin when he's stiff, you should advise him to see a doctor and get this dealt with surgically – hygiene-wise, it's NOT a good idea to have a foreskin that won't retract. Germs can breed under it, and there's risk of serious long-term inflammation.

If your partner still has a foreskin – in other words, if he's not circumcised – then you'll find that playing with it, using certain techniques common in Latin countries, is a good way of getting him going.

Obviously, you won't be able to do this if he's circumcised – as is the case with the majority of males in the USA, in Moslem countries and in Israel. Throughout the rest of the world, circumcision is becoming increasingly rare, and the odds are that your man will have an intact foreskin that you can play with as detailed in Chapter Four.

In the 21st century, many American males are getting irate about the fact that their parents had this pleasurable bit of their anatomy chopped off. They're trying to re-grow their foreskins by attaching small weights to the skin of their willies – with the object of stretching it. This is NOT something that I would recommend doing except under close medical supervision.

ITS SHAFT

The shaft is the main part of your bloke's penis – hopefully standing up proud and curved, and curiously like a banana in appearance. The shaft is the part that you really need to rub in order to make a chap climax, since the nerve-endings in it are closely linked to the orgasm centres in the spinal cord and brain.

A lot of people think there's a bone in it, but there isn't. It just contains three hollow cylinders – that start filling with blood when your man thinks about sex, or when you begin to stimulate him with your fingers, lips or tongue.

So all that happens in an erection is that his prick becomes totally engorged with blood, looking as though it's about to burst. (Don't worry – it won't.) It is completely normal for the veins on the shaft to stand out strongly from the surface of the skin. The more they stand out, the more enthusiastic he is about what you're doing to him.

SEX PLAY

ITS PLEASURE RIDGE

This is the name that I give to the long crest or eminence which runs down the heart side of his cock – starting at the heartstring, and continuing down to the very base of the organ. Turn back to the illustration on page 15 and you will see what I mean.

Intensely pleasurable sensations come from having this ridge stimulated, once erection has been achieved so that the whole ridge has the feel of being tight as a drum. Next time your man's penis is stiff, try the effect of running the moistened pads of your fingers up and down his pleasure ridge. He'll enjoy it, I promise you.

And later in the book, I'll show you ways of using your fingertips on either side of the ridge in order to produce very agreeable sensations indeed...

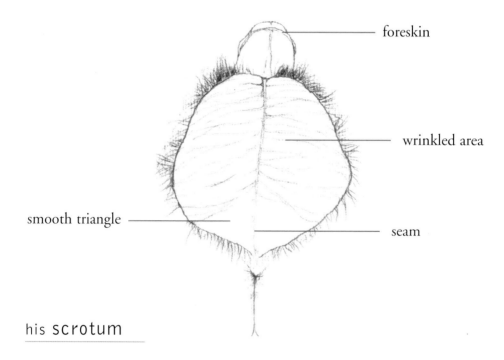

foreskin

wrinkled area

smooth triangle

seam

his **scrotum**

YOUR PARTNER'S SCROTUM

Have a look at the illustration above, that shows a very unusual view of a man. In fact, it's a view that has been seen by very few males indeed (apart from gay men, of course), and not many men know that this is what they look like from underneath.

We're gazing, of course, at the underside of your partner's balls – or rather, at his SCROTUM, which is the pouch of skin that contains them.

It's not widely known that the scrotum is actually quite an erotic area of the male body. As a woman, you may like to reflect on the fact that it's the exact equivalent of your own vaginal lips – so you would expect it to be a source of some pleasure.

It is divided into two totally different parts: a WRINKLED AREA, and behind that a SMOOTH TRIANGLE. Stroking and kissing the wrinkled area is nice for a man, but unlikely to start any fireworks.

The smooth triangle is exquisitely sensitive and touching it with your fingertip or tongue-tip may actually make your guy leap in the air!

Curiously enough, many men are quite unaware that this smooth triangular area exists because it's hidden from their eyeline – so your man may get a bit of a surprise when you first stroke it.

It's possible that you may have difficulty seeing it yourself if your partner is very hairy. So if by any chance you're into shaving (as some couples are), this is quite a good way of revealing his little super-sensitive triangle to your gaze.

You'll see from our drawing that there's a seam that runs straight through the smooth triangle. It's a continuation of the pleasure ridge of the penis and, like the pleasure ridge itself, it's darker than the skin – its actual colour depends on your man's race. Stroking it is nice for him.

Unless your guy is most unusual you are NOT likely to bring him to orgasm by stimulating any part of his scrotum. Working on his scrotum is just a nice little extra which will help to increase his enjoyment of a loving bedtime session with you.

HIS BALLS

I haven't yet mentioned stimulating your partner's balls (testicles) which are contained within the scrotum. This is quite a nice thing to do for him, and later on I'll be showing you certain techniques of testicle-stimulation (and also warning you against some dangerous ones which daft people go in for!)

Again, stroking, licking or kissing the balls isn't very likely to bring him to a climax, but it's a nice, loving act to perform for a chap. Always take it easy, because the testicles are the most TENDER organs in a man's body.

SEX PLAY

HIS PERINEUM

Your man's perineum (say it 'Perry – KNEE – um') is the area immediately behind the scrotum. It's a very sensitive and much neglected area – in both sexes. (Yes, women have a perineum too.) Pay it a little attention, and you'll find that your man enjoys the sensations which result.

In general, it's a good idea to begin by putting your fingertip on the seam (see the illustration on page 18) which divides his scrotum in two – and then work gradually backwards to the point where his bottom begins.

HIS PROSTATE

A man's prostate gland is about the size of a horse-chestnut, and the only way you can get at it is by slipping a well-lubricated finger up his bottom and pressing on the FRONT wall of his rectum, as explained in Chapter Twelve.

This certainly does produce some highly unusual feelings – as well as helping some guys with erection difficulties or problems in climaxing.

But there are some hygiene risks associated with this technique, so please don't try fingering your man's prostate till you've read the medical advice in Chapters Eleven and Twelve.

HEALTH WARNING

If you or your man notice any of the following abnormal signs in his sex organs, he MUST go and see a doctor right away:

- A swelling or lump in his balls. This is particularly vital in the twenty to forty age group, because that's when cancer of the testicle is most common.
- A raw sore on his penis – even if it's totally painless.
- Warts – and don't have sex with him till they've all been treated, since warts are infectious.
- A discharge from the tip of his cock – again, don't have sex with him until this has been cured by a doctor.

In fact, if you think you can see or feel ANY abnormality in the genital organs, it's always best to get a medical check-up – just in case.

the anatomy of

sex play

for men

A QUICK COURSE IN FEMALE ANATOMY

Here's my diploma course in female sexual anatomy. Please: approach these delicate and beautiful organs with care.

Don't charge at them like a rhino on heat. Instead, I would suggest that one evening when you and your lover are feeling tender and close, you agree between you that you will both inspect the various bits and pieces very slowly – preferably in a nice warm room, and with the aid of a small mirror, so that SHE too can see what her anatomy's like.

Incidentally, when you're feeling inside her, do please use plenty of lubrication; that'll make things a lot more comfortable for her.

YOUR PARTNER'S VISIBLE BITS AND WHAT TO CALL THEM

The area which you can see when you look at your partner fairly and squarely between the legs is medically known as her vulva. In practice, no one except doctors uses this word very much, and in many countries it's a term that's quite unknown to the average person.

So it's much more likely that you and she will be happy referring to her external parts by one of the truly popular and centuries-old names – such as cunny, cunt, quim, muff, twat, honey-pot or even fanny. But, don't employ that last word if you're in bed with somebody American – in the USA, it means 'bottom' or 'ass'.

Incidentally, it's worth noting that most people use these words to mean both the external AND the internal part of the female sex organs – that is, the vulva AND the vagina. So, a passionate woman might well say 'Please stroke my cunt' (meaning her vulva), or 'Darling, slip your finger up my cunt' (meaning her vagina). Either usage is correct, according to students of Anglo-Saxon etymology.

It is possible that you and/or the woman you love may be unhappy about using these blunt terms in bed. If so, then all you have to do is make up a nice, loving expression of your own. Maybe something along the lines of 'rosebud' or 'rosette' – after all, the vulva is a bit like a flower, isn't it? These intimate pet names can be a real source of fun and mutual bonding to a couple, especially if you're both aware that no one else knows your secret word. A doctor once wrote to me to say that she and her husband used the term 'schedule' to mean her vagina. Why? Because from

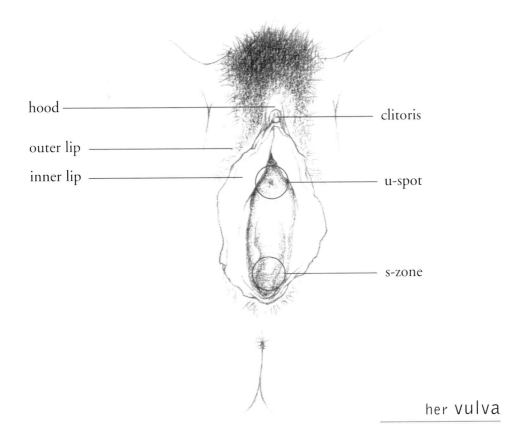

hood — clitoris
outer lip — u-spot
inner lip — s-zone

her vulva

time to time he'd say to her: 'Look, I know you're awfully busy with the practice, love, but could you fit me into your schedule?' Which she very gladly did.

In a moment I'm going to reveal all the mysteries of the vulva to you, so that you can check them out by inspecting your partner. But first one quick word of warning. As a man, you may not be aware that very large numbers of women feel very badly about their quims – and wrongly think that they are ugly or repellent. So when making a tour of inspection – or, indeed, when going in for the sex play techniques described in this book – it's a good idea to REASSURE your partner, and to tell her how beautiful you find all her bits.

She may take some convincing, especially if (like many girls) she was

23

programmed during childhood into the daft notion that everything about the human body is wonderfully designed and aesthetically pleasing, *except* the female genitals!

All the external features of the delightful feminine apparatus are shown in the illustration on page 23. So let's run through them one by one.

HER PUBIC HAIR

The pubic hair, or maidenhair as it's often called, is as a rule roughly triangular in shape, but it doesn't matter if it isn't. Many women – and men – don't realize this, and think there's something wrong if it doesn't conform to Euclid's specifications for an equilateral triangle.

It's an unfortunate fact that many people's ideas about the 'right' shape for the maidenhair are conditioned by seeing photos of pin-up girls. They don't realize that these young women have usually had their pubes carefully shaved or plucked before appearing in front of the camera – so as to conform to some mythical triangular norm. At the moment, you simply could not make a career as a nude model unless you had your pubic hair shaped into a triangle, which is a pretty crazy situation.

So please reassure your partner if her hair is box-shaped or splodgy or goes down the inside of her thighs or up towards her navel. It doesn't matter. In Chapters Three and Five, we'll be learning ways to use her pubic hair to enhance her sexual pleasure.

HER OUTER LIPS

Just like a mouth, the quim has LIPS – an outer set and an inner set. The outer set are the exact equivalent of your scrotum, sir – which is why they look a bit wrinkly and ragged. Again, many women think disappearance is abnormal. It isn't – so reassure your partner as you caress her.

Stimulating her outer lips with your finger, lips or tongue is quite nice for her. But, just as stroking a man's scrotum won't give him a climax, don't expect your partner to produce orgasms from that kind of stimulation alone.

But there are interesting and pleasure-giving ways of *stretching* the outer lips – as you'll discover if you keep reading.

HER INNER LIPS

Just inside those outer lips, the inner lips are shyly peeking out. In fact, if your partner has had babies they may well stick out quite far.

These are the little lips which wrap themselves quite tightly round your cock during intercourse, so it's not surprising that they're very sexually charged – especially when you realize that embryologists say that they are the exact female equivalent of the lower part of your penis.

We'll be discussing ways of stimulating them in Chapters Three, Five and Seven. But if you're inspecting and touching them as you're reading this, bear in mind that it's much more comfortable for the lady if you run a *moistened* finger, rather then a dry one, over the inner lips.

HER CLITORIS

Caressing her clitoris (as shown in the illustration overleaf) is a really lovely and loving thing for you to do for your partner. I've spent the last twenty years of my medical career in trying to teach the public where the clitoris is – and this book shows you what to do with it!

But if – like many people who write to me – you're not totally clear where it's located, just have another look at the illustration on page 23. You'll observe that the clitoris is situated right where the two inner lips meet at the top.

It's actually much smaller than most men and women think. In fact, most of the time it looks very like a little pink lentil. (Incidentally, it's pink in *all* races.) Even when it's sexually stimulated, it doesn't become all that big. You may have read that it 'gets erect like a penis', but in actuality the visible part of an erect clitoris is only about the size of a garden pea.

Recent work done by an Australian anatomist suggests that the 'hidden' part of the clitoris is much bigger than previously thought. She claims that the 'roots' of the clitoris run several centimetres down towards the thighs. So stroking to the SIDE of the visible part of the clitoris may help arouse your partner.

The clitoris really is the most sexually sensitive organ in the female body: indeed, for most women it's the real key to their sexual response. But, as I'll be showing you later in this book, you can't just press it and assume that the lady will enjoy what you're doing – life is more complex than that, I'm afraid.

SEX PLAY

Furthermore, recent research has shown that many females require both clitoral AND vaginal stimulation at the same time if they're going to really enjoy themselves. Fear not, gentlemen: it is possible to stimulate her clitoris and her vagina simultaneously, as you will discover shortly…

By the way, a further glance at the illustration on page 23 will show you that the clitoris is partly hidden by a tiny fold of tissue called the 'hood'. This is the equivalent of a man's foreskin – and the clitoris itself is the exact anatomical equivalent of the head of his penis. So, it's scarcely surprising that the clit is such a sexually charged area, is it?

HER U-SPOT

Now let's move on to a recent discovery – the female U-spot. Look again at our illustration on page 23 and, if practicable, compare it simultaneously with your partner's vulva.

About 1.75 inches (4.5 cm) directly down from her clitoris, you'll observe that there's a tiny HOLE. This is called the *urinary opening* and, not to put too fine a point on it, it is where she pees from. It's a small opening, quite like the slit at the tip of your own cock, but with a tiny beak jutting out at the lowest part of it, so as to direct the urine flow forwards.

Recent research in America, particularly by Professor Kevin McKenna and his colleagues at the Northwestern University Medical School in Chicago, has suggested that the area round the wee hole is an important sexual zone. Author Alexandra Penney, in her book *How to Make Love to a Man (Safely)* has christened it 'the U-spot'.

The approximate area of the U-spot is shown by the upper CIRCLE in the

caressing her clitoris

illustration on page 23 – in other words, it's all round the urinary opening. My own research suggests that quite a few women do like having this region stroked or kissed, but it would be a mistake to think that the U-spot is the orgasmic discovery of the late twentieth century. Really, I'd say that it's just another pleasant spot on the vulva – and well worth exploring (along the lines described in subsequent chapters) *provided you bear in mind that it may not work.*

For instance, the popular British magazine *New Woman* asked seven readers to locate and twiddle their U-spots. Three of them felt nothing at all except soreness or (in the case of a barrister called Alexandra) 'an overwhelming urge to pee'. The others expressed only moderate interest, with the exception of a speech therapist called Diana who reported: 'I became swamped with arousing feelings. It became quite intense and, combined with clitoral stimulation, I had a powerful orgasm.'

Good for Diana. But personally I agree with Jane Alexander, author of the *New Woman* survey, who very sensibly says to women:

> 'By all means play with your U-spot, G-spot, every spot you can find, provided it feels good. Explore your body and find out what feels right for you; get your partner to go exploring and see if he can come up with anything exciting.'

A brief word of warning: if you DO use the techniques which I'll be describing for stimulating her U-spot, you must take great care about *hygiene*. Prodding dirty fingers against her urinary opening could possibly give her a painful attack of cystitis – so wash them first. Do try to avoid introducing any infection into this area.

HER S-ZONE

Now we come to the S-zone or stretch-zone. You can see where it is by looking at the LOWER circle in the illustration on page 23 – and also the illustration of a woman's *internal* organs on page 30.

Let's put it quite bluntly: *most women like to be stretched*. This fact is not well known to men; as a sex we tend to have the idiotic delusion that what females desperately want is a LONG penis. This is simply not true.

But, size IS important, contrary to what so many well-meaning newspaper articles may tell you! My own very extensive sex surveys have confirmed that – other matters being equal – many women do tend to prefer a THICKER willy. Yes, thicker – not longer.

Why do they like thickness? Because a broad cock *stretches* the area round the opening of their vaginas – the area which I've labelled the S-zone in those illustrations you've been studying so carefully.

Indeed, quite a few females find difficulty in reaching orgasm unless this zone is stretched – and their clitorises are being simulated at the same time.

Why? Well the reason is simple. There's a wealth of erotic nerve endings in the OUTER 2 or 3 inches (5 or 7 cm) of the vaginal tube. There are relatively few in the INNER part of that tube – the part up near the cervix.

Indeed, some people in the media have gone so far as to assert that women have *no* sensation in the upper reaches of the vaginal tunnel. That certainly isn't true: any gynaecologist will tell you from personal experience that a lot of female patients experience strong sensations of both touch and pain from the upper part of the vagina.

But it is in the LOWER part of the vaginal barrel that women have nerve-endings which – given the right circumstances – are just longing to be stretched apart.

Don't get the wrong idea, though. If you're the sort of guy who believes that the quickest way to a lady's heart is to ram a 4-inch (10-cm) diameter vibrator up her, then you'd better think again! These are delicate tissues we're talking about, and they have to be stretched skilfully, gently and lovingly. I'll be showing you how to do this with your fingers, and through other means, later in the book.

HER INSIDE BITS

Now let's turn to the non-visible bits of a woman's cunny, the most important parts of which are shown in the illustration on the next page.

HER VAGINA

The vagina is basically a lovely, well-cushioned tube which is perfectly designed for accommodating a man's penis; it has no other biological function. Contrary to what many people think, it doesn't help the process of childbirth at all.

SEX PLAY

inside her
vagina

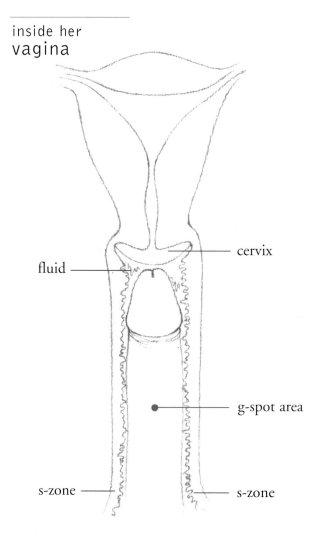

fluid

cervix

g-spot area

s-zone — — s-zone

It's much wider than most men and women imagine. And when a lady is sexually excited, it balloons out quite a bit so that it becomes very easy to slip several fingers inside it – as we'll be doing in the advanced sex play techniques described in Chapter Three.

It also *lengthens* during sexual excitement, so there should be room inside it for virtually any size of penis. If you look again at the illustration here, you'll see that during intercourse the erect cock more or less reaches as far as the end of the vagina. (In the case of a larger male organ, the vagina would expand further.)

You'll also note from the same picture that those nice, cushiony vaginal walls are producing big drops of fluid. These are the famous love juices which so pleasantly lubricate both intercourse and sex play. Oddly enough, doctors were completely muddled as to where these drops of fluid came from until the famous American sex researchers Masters and Johnson developed their well-known intra-vaginal camera, which took pictures inside the cunny during sexual excitement and conclusively showed that the liquid was coming out of the vaginal walls.

I need hardly say that in order to make your partner's vaginal liquid flow you must:

- Romance her.
- Cuddle her.
- Make her feel good and relaxed.
- Give her lots of sex play – concentrating mainly on the clitoris techniques described in the next few chapters. As a rule, it's not a good idea to put your finger inside till she's really flowing freely with those agreeable vaginal juices.

HER G-SPOT

The same illustration (see opposite page) shows you roughly where her G-spot is located in the front wall of her vagina. So if you're a bloke, look at a point about half-way up your own cock – on the belly side of it. *When you're inside her, that point is very close to where her G-spot is.*

But in practice, it's very, very difficult to exert any pressure on the G-spot area with your penis. However, it's quite easy to do it with your fingertips, and I'll be showing you how to achieve that in the next chapter.

I'm glad to say that skilled pressure in this area does produce very pleasant and unusual sensations in most women – though not all. Furthermore, if you get the G-spot caress right, it's often a great help to your partner in reaching orgasm.

HER CERVIX

Her cervix is the nice, soft knob located at the top end of the vagina – you can see it in the illustration on the opposite page.

If you've never felt it before, then what you need to do is to slip TWO fingers – the index and middle ones – gradually into her vagina. If you try it with just one finger, you probably won't be able to reach far enough. Obviously, make sure the fingers are well-lubricated.

You'll now feel something like the tip of a nose or the tip of a plump thumb, just on your fingertips. That's the cervix.

Many women don't seem to have very much in the way of nerve-endings in the cervix, and therefore feel neither pleasure nor pain there. But a lot of others do like having the cervix stroked or gently moved around – in the way that I'll explain in the next chapter.

SEX PLAY

31

HER OVARIES

If you look at the illustration on page 61, you can see where your partner's ovaries are located. They're the exact female equivalent of your balls – so treat them with respect!

It is possible to cause PAIN by prodding them too energetically, either with your penis or during sex play. If this happens, stop whatever you're doing and try something else, if your partner is happy to continue.

But it is also possible to produce a certain amount of pleasure by using the very skilled ovary caress which we'll come to in Chapter Three.

HER PERINEUM

Her perineum is the little area of skin located between her vagina and her bottom.

If she's in the right mood, stroking or tickling it may give her quite a lot of nice, sexy feelings. And when you slap her lower rump with your hand pointing downwards, or perhaps goose her, it's on her sensitive perineum that the tips of your fingers will land.

But because this is such a sensitive area, do have a care. The reason why both women AND men tend to leap a mile when somebody gooses them is simply that there are so many rather explosively-triggered nerve-endings in this tiny patch of skin. Suddenly poking it at the wrong moment could well produce outrage or anger, instead of a pleasurable response – so watch it.

HER BOTTOM

It's an undeniable fact of life that the anus (the opening of the rectum) is liberally supplied with erotic nerve-endings – in both men and women.

Indeed, women's bottoms are so inextricably entangled with their sexual responses that they actually go into *spasms* at the moment of climax! If you ever happen to be watching your loved one's rear end while she's coming, you'll be able to observe the series of powerful contractions of her anus which are one of the most reliable indications that orgasm is occurring (Very difficult to fake, incidentally…)

Now it is most unfortunate that the rectum is one of the dirty areas of the body – quite unlike the vagina and the penis, which are actually very CLEAN parts. To be blunt, there are often quite a lot of germs to be found in the anal area.

Nonetheless, a very large number of women do derive great pleasure from having their bottoms stimulated during sex play, or indeed intercourse.

In one of my British national sex surveys, 24 per cent of women said that they enjoyed having their botties touched up at times. And a number of them made the important point that if their man did this to them during sexual intercourse or sex play, it often helped to tip them over into a climax.

Well, that's fine. But if you're going to give your partner a spot of postillionage – which is the erudite word for touching up the bottom – you need to obey certain strict hygiene rules. These are explained in the sections on postillionage in Chapters Eleven and Twelve.

HEALTH WARNING!

Whenever you're toying with your loved one's personal parts, do always keep an eye out for any of the following danger signs. If a woman has any of these, she should see a doctor right away:

- A raw place on her vulva which doesn't heal up within a couple of days.
- Any unexplained LUMP on her vulva.
- Swollen glands in her groin (just to one side of the pubic hair).
- Warts in the opening of her vagina.
- Unexplained bleeding *provoked by sex*.
- Unexplained bleeding *after the menopause*.
- Unexplained bleeding *between periods*.
- An irritating or nasty-smelling discharge.
- A lump in her breast.
- Any odd change in the appearance of her nipple – or puckering in the skin of her breast.

Getting to know your partner's body during sex play can help you spot when something is going wrong healthwise. I'm not exaggerating when I say that you could even save her life.

SEX PLAY

finger
techniques for
a man to
use on a
woman

PLEASE BE GENTLE

So in this chapter we're going to look at nice things which men can do to women with their fingers. Just like in the illustration on the next page!

The finger caresses really are the most important things for any man to know about in bed. Indeed, it's a little difficult to see how anyone could ever become a good lover without having some basic knowledge of them. Yet very large numbers of men never use them, and then wonder why their wives/fiancées/girl friends remain unsatisfied. Luckily for you, dear male reader, by the time you've finished reading this chapter you'll be pretty familiar with most of the vital methods of touching up with the fingers (and thumbs). And I hope they will prove of great value to you in improving your relationship with your partner.

But first, a brief word of warning. Do please be GENTLE with your loved one – especially when you start to try out these techniques on her. Remember that the area of her body that you're dealing with is very easily hurt.

Sure, it has thousands and thousands of erotic nerve-endings – but it also has many nerve fibres which transmit PAIN. So for heaven's sake, don't bash the poor woman's vagina about! Treat it lovingly and carefully, as though it were the most important object in the world (and there are many males who would say that it is…).

A good plan is to TELL her what you're doing – in a loving, warm, erotic way, of course – rather than springing it as a sudden surprise on her. If she's in any doubt about what you mean, you can always give her this book so she can hold it in her hand and check, by looking at the illustrations, that you've got it right.

HOW WOMEN VARY

Sorry: just another brief warning before we kick off. Please bear in mind that women are not machines; they don't respond in (say) the way that a motorbike does when you kick-start it.

And when I say that they vary, I mean two separate things:

- First of all, individual females vary a lot from *each other*. A finger technique may be sensational for one woman, but do practically nothing for another one – even though they're both perfectly normal. So, just because a particular finger-frig worked wonderfully for somebody who was in your life five years ago, don't assume that it'll be just as brilliant for your present partner.

- *Secondly, many women vary a lot from day to day – or even from hour to hour – in their sexual responses. I assure you, sir, this really is essential to bear in mind: your wife or partner may absolutely love having her clitoris touched up at ten past three on a Sunday afternoon – but at half past four, she might find it boring or even unpleasant. She could still be feeling raunchy but she may well prefer that you do something totally different to give her enjoyment.*

Therefore, do vary these finger techniques, and be prepared to switch to lip or tongue play if you're not getting results. Above all, be guided by your partner and let HER tell you exactly where to move your fingers, depending on how she feels at that moment.

Similarly, do take her advice on how firmly (or how gently) you should press – and how fast (or how slowly) you should move your fingers and thumbs. Good luck!

GET LUBRICATED

It goes without saying that you need plenty of lubrication for these finger-play methods. Just imagine: would YOU like a dry finger shoved firmly into one of your orifices?

A woman who has been lovingly romanced, complimented, kissed and cuddled *before you go anywhere near her genitals* will start producing that lovely, dewy, natural lubrication which helps to make sex so easy and so pleasant.

But it's important to appreciate that a woman isn't like a can of lubricating oil – which you only have to squeeze to make the drops come out. While some women pour forth love juices fairly easily, others don't, particularly at certain times of the month when the secretions become less copious.

So I'd strongly recommend that when you're embarking on finger-frigging, you give her natural juices a little help. Licking your fingertips is a good way of doing this; for saliva (yours or hers) is Nature's way of augmenting the love juices.

In addition, skilled men do often make use of ARTIFICIAL lubricants on their

SEX PLAY

fingers. In most Western countries nowadays, you can buy these creams, jellies and lotions from pharmacies or sex shops without any need for embarrassment. But, do try to steer clear of highly-coloured, flavoured or scented products – which could just possibly cause a painful sensitivity reaction in your partner's sex organs (or yours). In general, the blander and milder the product the better.

Should you use Vaseline (petroleum jelly) as so many couples do? That's perfectly OK – as long as you're not going to have intercourse with a condom afterwards. The reason? Vaseline rots little holes in condoms.

CLITORIS TECHNIQUES

The first group of techniques that I want to tell you about all involve the lady's clitoris. Let me reiterate that before you go anywhere near this important little organ, you MUST make sure that your partner is feeling warm, romantic – and interested in sex.

And you MUST make sure that there is lubrication all round her clitoris.

If her vaginal juice is beginning to flow freely, then scoop up a little of that nice stuff on the pads of your first two fingers and apply it just above her 'clit' so that it trickles down over it. If there isn't quite enough vaginal fluid, then follow the advice I gave in the previous section and use your fingertips to apply a little saliva or a generous dollop of an artificial lubricant on to the same area.

OVER THE TOP

This is clitoris technique number one. You can see exactly what you should do in the illustration on page 40.

As you'll observe, the idea is to put the pad of your index finger just above your partner's clitoris. Then you move your finger quite rapidly up and down – so that it travels about $^1/_2$ to 1 inch (1 to 2 cm) in either direction.

using your
middle finger

When it reaches its lowest point, your fingertip should just about be touching the very topmost part of her clitoris, so that your contact with it is very slight indeed.

That's because the clit is a very sensitive organ – so it may well be that your partner doesn't want you to put any pressure on it at the very start of your sex play session.

Though you may find this hard to believe, with practice it's quite easy to move your forefinger up and down at a rate of over 350 times a minute! This is not as fast as the average vibrator, but it does give a woman very pleasant sensations indeed. However, for heavens' sake, do ASK her whether she'd like it faster or slower. Ask her too, whether she'd like you to press more heavily – or more lightly.

You'll see that our illustration shows a man doing the Over the Top technique to a woman from above – which is easy if you're lying beside her in bed, or sitting alongside her on a sofa. But if you're sitting or lying at a LOWER level than her, you can equally well do the Over the Top technique from below – that is, with your forefinger pointing upwards.

Incidentally, in order to see what you're doing you may find it helpful to follow the example of the chap in our picture, and *spread* your lover's outer lips with your other fingers. Or you can get her to join in the fun and spread them for you!

BY THE SIDE

This is also a very simple technique, and a good one to try in the early stages of a relationship. As you'll observe from the illustration shown on the next page, all that it involves is putting the pad of your finger ALONGSIDE the woman's clitoris and moving it rapidly up and

over the
top

clitoris

down. I'd recommend that you just touch the edge of the clitoris – but don't venture on to the organ itself unless and until she wants you to.

Again, this is because it's a sensitive structure – you shouldn't blunder on to it clumsily and risk upsetting its owner.

ROUND AND ROUND

Our third clitoral technique is also a simple one to master. I've noticed that many women instinctively use it themselves when they're masturbating (as in the illustration overleaf) – so that's a pretty good recommendation!

Most women seem to use two fingers for this method of stimulation, but there's no reason why you shouldn't use one – or even three – if you want to. However, the illustration on the next page shows the pads of the index and middle fingers being used to pleasure a lady.

All you do is sweep those well-moistened fingerpads round and round the whole area of the clitoris – either clockwise or anti-clockwise as you prefer (or even alternating between the two).

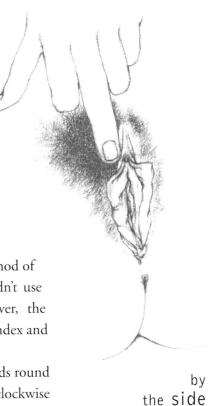

by
the **side**

If you're in any doubt that what you're doing is right, just get her to put HER hand on your wrist and guide you. Remember: she knows what she likes!

SPOT ON

Don't try this one unless you've already got your partner thoroughly warmed up – and preferably panting with desire.

If you've read the earlier part of this chapter, you'll know why the *kitzler* (as the Germans call it) is a tender and highly *temperamentvoll* little organ. Jumping on it when it isn't ready is most unlikely to produce good results; indeed, it may produce bad ones.

SEX PLAY

round
and round

But once your partner is excited and lubricating well, then go ahead and try the Spot On technique. Just put a damp forefinger right on her clitoris and begin to rub it.

You'll probably find it best to start slowly and with a light touch. But as matters progress, the kitzler's owner may start to insist that you rub harder and faster. Whatever she wants, go with it – making sure as you do so that you keep everything as moist as you possibly can, so that you increase the pleasurable sensations for her *without* causing any trauma to her clitoris.

Incidentally, I am very serious about this business of avoiding trauma to the poor, battered old clitoris. Years ago in the medical journal *World Medicine*, I published what I believe was the world's first description of a condition called 'clitoral haematoma', which is caused by excessively forceful rubbing (particularly DRY rubbing) of the organ.

What happens is that the friction causes a small blood clot to form inside the clitoris. This hurts – and it goes on hurting for several days. During this time, the clitoris is swollen and red-looking. Fortunately, the problem nearly always cures itself – something goes 'pop', the blood leaks out, and that's it.

Sorry to introduce such an alarmist note, but I hope what I've just said will be a warning to all you males out there. When rubbing that little pink clitoris *keep it moist*. And if it's hurting, STOP!

By the way, a final useful tip about clitoral techniques: nearly all of them will work even better if you use a spare hand to draw the lowest part of the skin of her tummy UPWARDS; this stretches the clitoris and intensifies the sensation. You can achieve much the same effect by firmly stroking her pubic hair upwards.

PROBING TECHNIQUES

Now we move on to my probing or thrusting techniques, which are more difficult to do well. So practise, practise, practise!

Also, please remember what we said in the Introduction to this book about (a) having very clean fingers; and (b) not having jagged nails. Now that your fingers are actually going INSIDE your loved one, it is very, very important indeed to make sure that they aren't going to do her any harm.

Probing or thrusting techniques aren't nearly as widely used as they should be. Most men seem to be vaguely aware that it's possible to imitate the action of the penis with your middle finger (which is the nearest thing you can get to a penis in length, among the various parts of your body).

But I have asked very sexually experienced women about their recollections of what past lovers did to them in bed, and most of these women say that very few blokes had the knowledge or the inclination to use the finger techniques which I'm now going to describe. And that's a pity – because these methods really are helpful in assisting a lady to obtain greater pleasure and satisfaction.

TOM THUMB

The first probing technique is the one I call Tom Thumb. As you can see from the illustration overleaf, it involves slipping your well-lubricated thumb between her (I hope) equally well-lubricated lips, so that it enters her vagina.

You may perhaps be surprised at the idea of putting your THUMB inside. After all, the thumb is quite short, isn't it? In most guys, it's only about two-thirds of the length of the middle finger – so you might think that it would be no use at all.

Quite wrong. Sophisticated women report that they often get intense pleasure from a male thumb pushed gently inside them. ('It's such a great help when I want to reach orgasm', said one well-known actress.)

Why? The reason is simple. The thumb is usually quite a bit thicker than the other fingers. As we'll see in a minute when we get on to my new vaginal stretching techniques, thickness is much more important than length. The thumb widens the outer part of the vagina much more than your other fingers can. So putting it inside will give your lover an agreeable sensation of fullness and bulk …

SEX PLAY

43

tom **thumb**

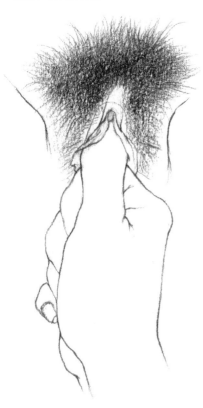

But having got it inside, what are you going to do with it? There are several possibilities:

- Having inserted it, you can simply keep it there for a bit – while you do other nice things to your partner, like kissing her, stroking her breasts or telling her she's lovely.
- You can sexily move it in and out, imitating the action of the penis with your thrusts. This works very well on most women, particularly if you turn your wrist so as to ensure that when you thrust really deeply, the part of your hand which is at the *base* of your thumb sort of nudges against your partner's clitoris.
- You can twist it round and round. I suspect that only a woman could have invented this method, because us blokes are so conditioned to think that only DEEP THRUSTING will satisfy a female. In fact, just twirling your thumb round softly and smoothly inside the lady you love will give her delightful sensations – for which she will be delighted to repay you (as soon as she's read Chapter Four).
- You can also waggle your thumb to and fro, so as to stimulate the back and front *walls* of her vagina – more about these walls in a moment.
- Finally, you can try out ALL the above thumb techniques with your partner facing *the other way up* – in other words, with her lying on her tummy, while you slip your thumb in from behind. Good luck.

MIDDLE FOR DIDDLE

Having learned how to probe sensitively with your thumb, you're now ready to move on to other probing and thrusting techniques.

You'll find that it's very easy to slip a moist middle finger into your partner's cunny, with your palm upwards – as shown in our illustration overleaf. Despite its lack of bulk around the base, this is the longest finger, so it really does give good results with thrusting motions. Indeed, many women can be brought to a climax simply by means of repeated thrusts with this finger.

Begin gradually, feeling your way, and assessing just what your partner wants you to do. Once she's comfortable and relaxed, you can begin to make your thrusts a little deeper and also speed them up. A very skilled lover can actually achieve a rate of well over 400 thrusts a minute, which is certainly a lot faster than you'd get during intercourse!

It may seem difficult to achieve such speeds at first, but it isn't really – once you grasp that you've just got to make a very fast, repetitive to-and-fro movement, which is curiously reminiscent of beating an egg… So far I haven't heard of any man getting Repetitive Strain Injury from pleasuring his lady this way, but you never know.

More seriously, here's an Important Warning. (I'm sorry I keep issuing these Important Warnings, but you don't want to damage your partner, do you?) If you're not very careful with the Middle for Diddle caress, you can easily cut the woman's vagina or vulva with your fingernail.

This sort of injury happens quite frequently, and it's very painful and distressing. It's much less likely to occur if your middle fingernail is neatly trimmed and/or filed. Also, it's less likely *if you take care not to pull your finger back too far when you withdraw it*. If you actually pull it completely OUT of the vagina, there's a very high risk that you'll jab her vulva, or even the skin round it, on the way back in. This hurts like hell. And if you cut her, you'll find that it's a very difficult place to put a Band-Aid …

Though I've said that you'll give very intense stimulation by moving your finger in and out very, very fast, there are plenty of women who often prefer this to be done much more slowly and languorously, preferably with plenty of turns and twists of your finger as it slides in and out.

SEX PLAY

Oh, yes – could you please note the position of the chap's forefinger KNUCKLE in our drawing? I know this may seem like rather a ludicrous technicality, but the fact that the knuckle is where it is means that it will keep nuzzling against the area of your partner's clitoris every time you thrust in. She will like this, I promise you. Honestly.

Finally, if you wish you can move on to two more advanced versions of Middle for Diddle:

1   Roll your hand over so that you insert your finger with palm downwards. Then thrust as before, but take it easy as control is not usually as good this way.

2   Invite your lover to lie on her front and gradually slip your middle finger in from behind – either palm upwards or palm downwards as she prefers. Then begin gentle thrusting.

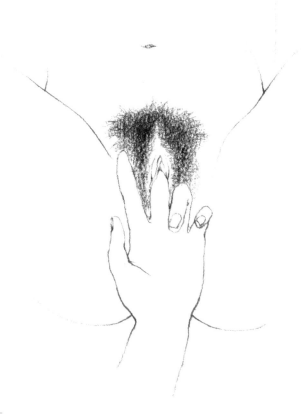

middle
for diddle

V-SIGN CARESS

Yes, it's possible that this technique is the origin of the famous rude two-finger sign which is so common throughout Britain and the Commonwealth – though not in America where, for some reason, rude gestures usually involve only ONE finger. In Italy, they use the whole arm – which definitely says something about the passion of the Italian character.

Anyway, what you do here is to gradually insert your index and middle fingers into the vagina of the woman you love – and then open them out a little. Obviously, you shouldn't open them out BEFORE you put them in. Look at the illustration on page 48 to see exactly what to do.

Once they're in, what can you do with them? Well, here's a selection of nice things which I'm sure will please your partner:

- Feel the SIDE walls of her vagina (left and right). These are areas which aren't all that often stimulated in other ways, so you will give her some unusual and agreeable feelings.
- Thrust the two fingers gently in and out. Note from our illustration that, while you do this, it's easy to make your thumb butt repeatedly against her clitoris.
- Use the two fingers to stroke her FRONT and BACK vaginal walls; these are very sensuous areas in many females.

Some years ago, an eccentric doctor in South America hired about two hundred women: then he and his nurse stroked the front and back walls of all their vaginas. Incredibly, the patients gave their consent to this bizarre experiment! At the end of it, they were asked to say whether they found stroking the front or the back wall more stimulating.

The majority preferred the front wall, but quite a substantial minority opted for the back one. Both types of stroking nearly caused orgasm in some cases, or so the good doctor claimed in a medical journal…

I don't think that this particular experiment is likely to be repeated – at least, not in places like Europe, America or Australia, where the medical authorities might not be too keen on it. But it does show that you may well be able to use the V-Sign

SEX PLAY

Caress successfully on either the back or the front wall of your loved one's vagina. A good tip is this: whichever wall you choose, start in the middle of it with both fingers together, and then spread them apart – taking your cue from your partner as to just how much pressure is comfortable.

When you're pressing on the BACK wall, this will give her all sorts of unusual sensations in her bottom or even far up into her rectum. Bear in mind that while a lot of women love such feelings, many others are quite embarrassed by them, and fear they may lose control or pass wind. So if that applies to YOUR partner, desist.

Similarly, using the V-Sign Caress on the FRONT wall of your partner's vagina will stimulate the region of her bladder, and make her feel as though she wants to pass water. Again, many women find this experience quite thrilling and 'naughty', but a few are embarrassed by it – so take care.

Incidentally, while doing the V-Sign Caress you may accidentally hit on the Famous Female G-spot – of which more in a few moments.

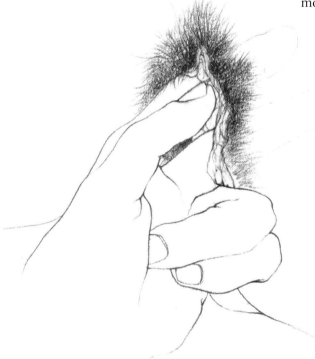

v-sign caress

STRETCHING TECHNIQUES

We now come to an important group of sex play caresses: the STRETCHING techniques.

What's the point of them? Well, in the last few years three things have become apparent to me:

1   A lot of women can't reach orgasm easily unless they have the clitoris and the vagina stimulated at the same time. This was confirmed by a recent survey carried out in the US by *Cosmopolitan* magazine.

2   The erotic nerve-endings in the vagina are concentrated near the opening – that is, in the first 2 or 3 inches (5 or 8 cm). And they are very, very receptive to stimulation.

3   Probably the best way of stimulating these vaginal nerve-endings is by STRETCHING them – in other words, by putting something with a fairly wide diameter into the vaginal opening.

Now you know why so many sexologists say that the LENGTH of a man's penis isn't important! Quite right – it's the width round the base that counts, because this is the part that dilates the vaginal opening. And if you ask a number of liberated women what sort of male organ they prefer, few of them will reply with the male fantasy of 'a really long one'. But many of them will say that – other matters being equal – they would prefer a THICK one. As a respondent to one of my national sex surveys wrote on her questionnaire: 'Us London ladies do like a spot of bulk …'

So STRETCHING the vaginal opening will help you to open up new worlds of pleasure for the woman in your life. Here (for the first time in print) I present some half-a-dozen sex play 'stretchers' which I hope that females everywhere will enjoy!

The first of these is called The Scissors…

SEX PLAY

THE SCISSORS

You can see the technique of the scissors stretch very clearly in the illustration here. In a way, it's quite like the V-Sign Caress, in that you slip two well-lubricated fingers – the middle and the index fingers – up your lover's quim.

But what you do now is different. *You simply spread the two fingers as wide apart as possible.* Then draw them back just a little bit towards you – and you will find that you are STRETCHING the opening of her vagina for her.

Provided that she is well-relaxed, she should find this very pleasant indeed. I'd recommend that you keep those two fingers there for a while, spreading out her opening as much as possible, while you do other agreeable things to her – like kissing her clitoris, or stroking round it with your other hand. Or, if such things take her fancy, get HER to stroke her clitoral area while you continue the stretching of her opening.

the **scissors** stretch

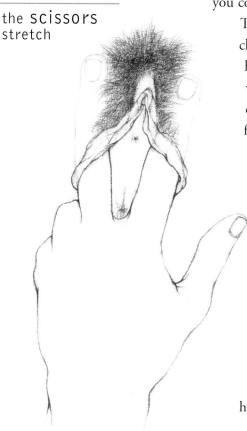

This double stimulation (stretching plus clitoris-stroking) is often of great benefit in helping a woman reach orgasm. In fact, some women just can't come unless both the clitoris and the S-zone ('S' standing for 'stretch') are getting their fair share of attention.

I have to admit that unless you have very strong hands, it's pretty difficult to keep your middle and index fingers forced wide apart for very long – especially if they're pressing against a powerful set of vaginal muscles!

Partly for that reason, I've invented a series of new stretching techniques which are even more effective than The Scissors, but less strain on the fingers. Let's have a look at them now.

THE VERTICAL STRETCH

There are two versions of this. The first is shown on this page. Obviously, before trying it you must make sure that your lover is relaxed, well-lubricated and receptive to what you're going to do.

She should be lying flat on her back, with thighs well apart. Lie next to her, facing her, and on your left side. Simply slip the fingers of your right hand into her – and then part them so that they stretch her vertically, as shown.

But much easier for you is the Two-Hand Vertical Stretch. Simply reach down with your LEFT hand and slip your moist index finger just a couple of inches (5 cm) inside her, curling it upwards round her pubic bone – which will feel firm to the touch of your fingertip. Next, reach down with your RIGHT hand and slip its index finger into the lowest part of her vaginal opening. Curl it a bit, so that it's pointing downwards.

If you've followed these slightly daft-sounding directions properly, your two hands will now be in a position to give her considerable pleasure. *All you have to do is draw your hands firmly apart.* This powerful motion will not hurt her – but it will put delightful pressure on her S-for-stretch zone.

the **vertical** stretch

What you do next is up to you – or, preferably, her! Wiggling your fingertips around is good; so is alternate relaxing and pulling apart of your hands. But if you're going to provide the type of double stimulation which is so effective in turning many women on – and assisting them to reach climaxes – then you and she may wish to combine the vertical stretch with other techniques which touch up the region of her clitoris.

You won't find this easy to do with your fingers – unless your left hand happens to possess the skills of a fairly high-grade contortionist. But it should be quite possible for you to caress her clit with your tongue or lips while your two hands are occupied with the Two-Hand Vertical Stretch. (If you're not sure how to do these oral caresses, please see Chapter Five.) Alternatively, your partner may fancy frigging herself with a dainty finger – or perhaps using a vibrator on her clitoris, as you manfully stretch her …

ST VALENTINE'S STRETCH

This is so called because it was invented on St Valentine's Day, under circumstances which I do not propose to describe here – or anywhere else. But they were romantic.

Anyway, St Valentine's Stretch is fairly similar to the Two-Hand Vertical Stretch, except that you create more erotic pressure on the S-zone, which with a bit of luck

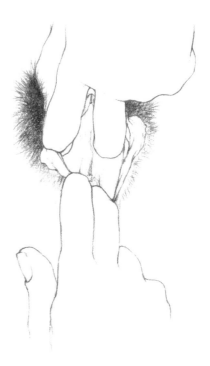

St
Valentines
stretch

she will like a lot. Also, it's less of a muscular strain for you, so you should be able to keep it up for longer, and have more time to introduce nice variations for her.

What do you do? Well, just have a look at the illustration. As you can see, it's a simple question of putting two moistened fingers in the top half of her vaginal opening – and two moistened fingers in the lower half.

Then draw the two hands apart as before, being guided by your partner as to how much stretching of her S-zone she wants. One good ploy is to stretch and release regularly every couple of seconds, thus giving her a delightful throbbing sensation in her vaginal muscles.

Also, by altering the distance between your middle and index fingers from time to time, you can vary the pleasurable sensations which you give her.

As in the case of the other S-zone stretchers in this section, you'll find it useful to combine the St Valentine's Stretch with other stimulatory techniques like those described in the later chapters of this book.

HORIZONTAL STRETCHES

We've also developed some ways of stretching the S-zone of the vaginal opening HORIZONTALLY. One way of doing this is shown in the illustration overleaf. Horizontal stretching produces a whole different bunch of sensations in a lady's quim, but they are actually very similar to what she feels when she's having intercourse with a chap who has a very thick penis. The sides of her opening are pressed wide apart, and all the nerve-endings in them should start sending pleasure signals to her brain.

So, gradually slip two moistened fingers from each hand into her cunny as shown in our drawing on the next page – and then draw them apart. Be guided by her as to the amount of pressure you should use, and do of course stop if she feels any pain at all. But this is unlikely, provided that she is relaxed, and enthusiastic about you and your love-making!

As a variation on the above, draw your fingers back a little bit towards you and concentrate on drawing her *inner lips* apart.

Another variation is to use just ONE finger of each hand to stretch her horizontally. If you use your middle fingers, this leaves your index fingers free to stroke some of the other areas of her opening.

SEX PLAY

the horizontal stretch

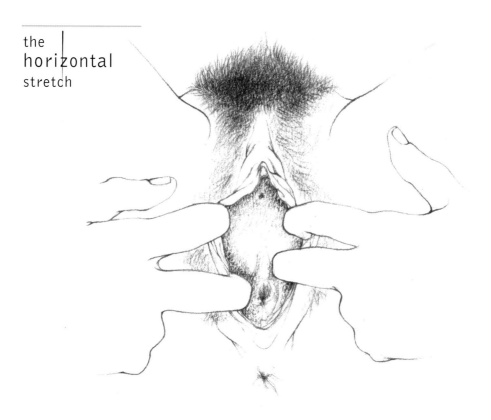

Your partner may also like it if you use just the *fingertips* of both hands to stretch her *outer* lips wide apart horizontally – thus spreading out all her secret charms to your view. Again, be guided by what SHE says feels good.

What can you do to accompany a horizontal stretch? Well, this group of techniques offers you an unrivalled opportunity to get at various of her intimate areas with your lips and tongue.

So, if you're lying or kneeling directly in front of her vagina and 'pulling her apart' with a horizontal stretch, your face is right in front of her opened-up vulva and you can give her a wonderful time by kissing or licking either her clitoris or the area now called the U-spot (see Chapter Two) – or by putting your tongue inside her vagina.

Alternatively, she may wish to use a vibrator on her clitoris while you're horizontally stretching her. Or, if her opening is wide enough, she may even want to pop a small vibrator up inside herself while you hold the sides apart.

In short, the two of you should be as inventive and as way-out as you fancy. Have fun!

THE OBSTETRICIAN'S HAND

I call this 'the Obstetrician's Hand' – which is an old medical term – because obstetricians and midwives do sometimes put the entire hand into the vagina in the way shown in the illustration here.

the
obstetrician's
hand

Now please use great caution in doing this one, because it does stretch your partner's opening very wide in all directions. Don't try it unless you and she have done plenty of other stretch techniques together in the past, so that she's completely used to them. It's vital that she feels thoroughly happy about what you're doing to her.

If she is nervous, don't try it – because if she doesn't relax fully, you may cause her pain instead of pleasure. That's more likely to happen in the case of a sexually inexperienced woman, especially if she's never had any children.

But women who like their sex (and particularly women who've had babies) are usually pleased by being introduced to this technique. The illustration says it all, really: just introduce your moistened fingers one by one into her cunny, with your palm facing upwards. Make absolutely sure that she's well aroused – and preferably *drenched* with vaginal love fluid – before you insert your final three fingers.

In practice, your hand will only go in about as far as the base of your thumb. DON'T force things – and if she suddenly feels uncomfortable and says 'Take it out', then take it out. But once she's comfortable with your hand inside her, the two of you can move on to whatever jolly options she chooses. For instance, if your left hand is happily wedged in her S-zone, you can use your right hand to frig her clitoris, to caress her nipples, or indeed to touch her up with a vibrator.

Once again, the double effect of stretching plus another form of stimulation is often highly effective in helping the woman reach orgasm.

DEEP INTERNAL TECHNIQUES

At this point we move on to loving caresses in which you put your fingers more deeply into your partner's agreeable honey-pot. Once again, be very sure that your hands are clean, and that includes your fingernails. And do not – repeat not – try these in-depth techniques until your lover is really dripping with lubrication and (if you will forgive a colloquialism for once) 'rarin' to go'.

If you haven't read the section on the vagina in Chapter Two, could I suggest that you go back and have a look at it now? And before you start trying to find G-spots, you should – with your partner's permission, of course – spend a good deal of time feeling around inside the deeper recesses of her quim with two thoroughly-lubricated fingers, so that both of you are thoroughly accustomed to your probing fingers being far inside her.

the
g-spot finder

THE G-SPOT FINDER AND MASSAGER

Now: the G-spot. There's some argument as to whether it's an actual organ (the equivalent of the male prostate gland) or not. Personally, I don't think it matters very much. What IS important is the fact that a lot of women do get very nice sensations if you stimulate this particular area. And in some of them, stimulation of the G-spot zone is of great assistance in helping them to reach orgasm.

Right, where is it? If you recall, back in Chapter Two I said that you can get an approximate idea of its location if you pick a point about half-way up the belly side of your erect penis – as shown in the illustration on page 30. That's the bit of you that is nearest to your lover's G-spot when your prick is inside her.

So, in order to (literally) put your finger on it, what do you do? Well, I've invented two methods of finding it:

1   When your partner is relaxed and happy, ask her to lie flat on her back. Make sure she is well lubricated. Now, with your palm *upwards*, slip your moistened forefinger about 2 to 3 inches (5 to 8 cm) inside her cunny. If you have very short fingers, you'll do better to use the middle one as well. Next, make a beckoning gesture with your finger – just like in the drawing. This will bring your fingertip against the FRONT wall of her vagina, under which you should be able to feel the distinctive hardness of her pubic bone.

    Press up really firmly with the pad of your index finger against that bone, then start to move your fingertip around in circles – covering roughly the area of a large coin.

    Now here's the trick: when your partner suddenly says 'Ooooh! That feels funny', you've reached the G-spot! I'll tell you more in a moment about the sort of feelings she'll experience. But first let me explain my other method of finding this special area.

2   This method, I feel, requires a certain sense of humour on her part – and yours. Invite her to settle herself comfortably on all fours on the bed. She's now face downwards, of course.

    Sit beside her, somewhere near her bottom. Now, holding your hand with your palm *downwards*, slip your finger into her vagina from behind. Go in far enough for TWO of the knuckles of your forefinger to disappear. (If at any time she says she's fed up and is finding this position undignified, do stop.)

    Now, crook your finger in a beckoning gesture as before. Once again, you will feel the hardness of her pubic bone. Rummage around on it with the pad of your finger until she reacts as above, and says she feels something unusual. But what *are* her feelings likely to be? Well, many women report

SEX PLAY

57

that at the beginning there's a sudden and rather surprising urge to pee. This is entirely natural – because you are in fact compressing your partner's little urinary pipe against her pubic bone. (This is very much as if she were compressing YOUR urinary pipe, which of course runs down through your penis.)

The sensation which she feels is a VERY strong one; indeed, some women do not like it at first, particularly if they're embarrassed by the idea that your pressure might make them pee. But if a lady perseveres – and if her man is gentle and understanding – she will usually begin to enjoy this rather strange new feeling. However, it may take the two of you many weeks to get things right, so that she feels totally happy with this intriguing but slightly alarming manoeuvre.

But what are you actually supposed to be DOING to her G-spot area, now that you've found it? Well, as always, I suggest that you take things gently. Don't vibrate your fingertip very fast as though you were frigging her clitoris. Instead, make slow, massaging movements:

- Round and round.
- From side to side.
- And up and down.

Try to cover an area about 2 inches (5 cm) across. But be guided by your partner who, as time goes by, will start to say things like: 'That's the spot… mmm… stay on there and just rub it firmly… up a bit… ' and so on.

If you have sensitive fingers, you may be able to discern a slight swelling in the region of the G-spot – especially when your partner gets excited. Although very little scientific research has been done on this, my own impression is that this swelling is part of a soft vertical ridge which runs down the front wall of the vagina. Rolling your fingertip across this ridge from one side to the other is likely to go down well with your partner.

What else can you do to her G-spot area? Well, you can put your thumb in and massage it with that, if you fancy. If you try this, you'll find that it leaves your other fingers admirably placed to rub her clitoris and other adjacent regions.

In fact, paying attention to her clitoris with your fingers or lips at the same time as you massage her G-spot is not a bad idea at all, especially if she wants to go for an orgasm. Some women can come just through G-spot massage alone, but many others need clitoral stimulation as well.

However, what is quite certain is that skilful pressure on the G-spot region does make it much EASIER for a lot of women to climax. So this fairly simple technique really is a major advance in helping the very large number of females who have trouble in getting an orgasm.

While we're on the subject of orgasm, one final point: there's a persistent rumour – often passed on by women during 'networking' – that if a man stimulates his partner to orgasm by working on her G-spot, she will shoot out a special 'sex fluid' when she comes.

Well, this whole business of female ejaculation is a very contentious one. Until quite recently, most doctors believed that women do NOT ejaculate at climax – and that if any fluid comes out, it is urine.

Erotic novels from as far back as the eighteenth century have taken a totally opposite viewpoint: their heroines usually *drench* the sheets with pints of sex fluid at the height of their passion!

Since about 1980, it has slowly become clear that quite a substantial minority of women do indeed shoot an appreciable volume of some clear or whitish fluid just at the moment when they come. Some of my gallant readers have attempted to send me samples through the mail…

But I'm afraid that at the time of writing, nobody really knows what this fluid is, or where it originates. It could well be from the G-spot region – especially if, as some people reckon, the G-spot is the female equivalent of the man's prostate gland.

The important thing to realize is that producing this interesting liquid at the moment of orgasm is perfectly NORMAL for many, many females. Sadly, a lot of women do not know this fact – so their entire sex lives have been blighted by desperate embarrassment that somebody will find out that they 'wet themselves' when they come.

Indeed, in my postbag I've had letters from women whose lovers have actually

SEX PLAY

59

LEFT them because they were disgusted that the woman appeared to urinate at the moment of orgasm. Isn't this crazy?

Fortunately, there are plenty of other guys who are absolutely delighted if a spot of sex play makes the woman suddenly pour out a dewy fluid when she climaxes! And very sensible of them…

As far as the G-spot area is concerned, one group of American experts says that 'the phenomenon [of ejaculation] seems to occur more frequently in women when the G-spot is stimulated.' So… why not stimulate it – and see what happens?

THE CERVIX CARESS

As we said in the chapter on female sexual anatomy, the cervix is that nice, softish at the top end of the vagina. Some women have sexy sensations in it, others don't.

But if the two of you are thoroughly accustomed to each other, and if your partner is happy to have you poking around at the top of her vagina seeking new places to stimulate, then the cervix caress is definitely worth a try.

Have a look at the drawing here and you'll get the general idea. All you have to do is:

1   Find her cervix.
2   Gently move it around with your fingertips.

If she likes this, all well and good. If she feels nothing, then clearly it's not worth continuing. And if by any chance she feels any pain or discomfort, then of course you should stop.

the
cervix caress

STROKING HER OVARIES

This is really the most advanced of all sex play techniques – and the most difficult to do. So if you can't master it, don't worry; there are plenty of other nice things in this book for you to do to your woman. But if you want to give it a try, here's what you do. First, have a look at the illustration together. Then slip two well-lubricated fingers into her vagina, and up to the top as shown. Provided your fingers are long enough, you should be able to reach the region just to the SIDE of her cervix.

If you then use the pads of your fingers to massage her vaginal wall at the point indicated in our picture, you may well be able to create some pleasant sensations for her. Obviously, if she doesn't like the feeling, you should leave it and go on to something else.

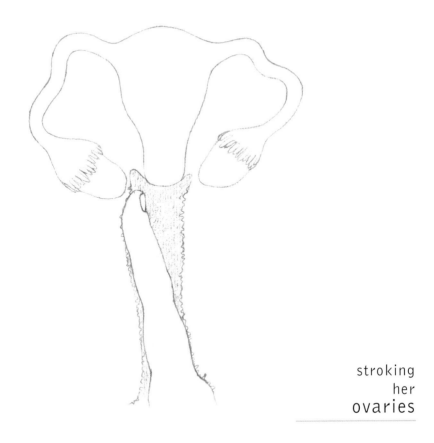

stroking
her
ovaries

COMBINING YOUR TECHNIQUES

In this chapter I've described many different ways of giving your partner pleasure by stimulating various parts of her cunny with your fingers.

But it's very important to understand two things:

• Most of these techniques take a long time to perfect – so practise, practise, practise!
• Many of them work best if you can manage to do *something else at the some time.*

Yes, a lot of women will respond better if you can give them the combined stimulation of TWO sex play techniques at once. This fits in very much with the recent American survey which shows that a lot of women need both vaginal *and* clitoral stimulation if they're going to climax easily

So, whenever the situation seems right, do try combining a vaginal technique of sex play – such as the new S-zone stretches detailed in this chapter – with stimulating the region around her clitoris.

Isn't it a pity that us guys have only got one pair of hands? Of course, some couples do 'recruit' another pair of hands – but that's a different story.

LET HER HELP!

But there is already another pair of hands in the bed with you – hers. And though it may surprise you, a lot of women are jolly keen to join in and help you while you're giving them a spot of quim-caressing.

Sorry if that shocks you. However, the fact is that most sexologists now reckon that a little self-masturbation by the lady during sex play is an excellent thing. And if she is used to masturbating, then there's no doubt that it really does help her get to orgasm…

So, if you are happily doing something nice to your lover's vagina (say, stretching her S-zone with your fingers or thrusting in and out), then don't hesitate to encourage her to – literally – lend a hand, and to frig her own clitoris if she wants to. Incidentally, it's often the case that orgasms produced in this way are particularly intense and satisfying.

masturbating
together

4

finger techniques for a woman to use on a man

GO FOR IT!

In this chapter we turn to the question of how to excite a MAN with the fingers. At this point, most sex books will go on and on interminably about how women 'should first seek out male erogenous zones which are far away from the genital area' – say, between his shoulder blades or on top of his bald patch.

This book does not do that.

Yes, dear female readers, this book recognizes one simple Law of Nature, which it is time that you knew about. It is this.

The average guy's idea of heaven is having a lovely woman holding his cock – or somewhere pretty close to it.

He doesn't particularly mind if you want to spend time stroking the nape of his neck or the end of his big toe, but what he REALLY wants you to do is to caress his penis, and the adjoining 'naughty bits'

This chapter will tell you exactly how to do that. Go for it.

BUT LEAVE MY MORE EXOTIC TECHNIQUES TILL LAST

However, I'd prefer you not to rush ahead to the more exotic and outrageous penis-stimulating methods which I'll be describing later in the chapter.

Please begin with simple techniques, such as the one shown on page 69 (The Cocktail Shaker) before you move on to some of my really *outré* inventions, like the U-spot Caress, the Häagen-Dazs Filler, or the techniques using ice, peppermint or ginger.

Why? Well, obviously it's best to start with easy and straightforward methods – and to make sure you've got them right – before you progress to more tricky ones.

Also, you don't want to terrify your poor guy by suddenly attacking him with the Perineal Pleaser, or even the Penisator, when he's not ready for it! After all, it's probable that no woman will ever have offered these extravagant finger-pleasers to him before in his life.

So – easy does it…

WHY YOU CAN'T HAVE TOO MUCH LUBRICATION

First of all, I'm going to let you into THE big secret of manipulating a penis successfully.

Every topless masseuse knows this trade secret, but unfortunately not many wives and girl friends do. It is this.

To be really good at finger-work with a guy's organ, you need lots of LUBRICATION. In fact, you can't have too much of it.

Why? Well, to begin with you have to appreciate that lubrication makes your fingers slide over his phallus much more easily – in precisely the same way that OIL makes almost *any* mechanism work more smoothly. If you don't believe this, then try a simple experiment: rub your fingertips rapidly across the back of your hand for ten seconds or so. Even if you have the smoothest skin in the world, you'll notice a certain amount of bumpiness and sticking. If you go on for long enough, there will be warmth – and possibly even a little pain.

Now slurp a spot of face cream (or something similar) on the tips of your fingers and try it again; obviously, you'll now find that they GLIDE across the back of your hand silkily and easily, with no discomfort at all. I assure you that the same thing will happen if you use a little lubrication on your man's penis.

The second reason for using what the sex-shops inelegantly call 'lubes' is this. They do actually protect your guy's delicate parts from trauma. As a woman, you may find that a bit difficult to believe! But the fact is that enthusiastic rubbing of a chap's *zizi* does tend to scrape off a good few layers of skin – sometimes with quite painful results. That's why many men who lead active sex lives complain that their organs are red and sore after a hectic night's love-making. Some (particularly the middle-aged) develop fairly raw patches, which they get quite worried about.

All of this can be prevented by the use of lubricants. But WHAT lubricants?

Well, Nature's own lubricant is saliva – and if you use lots of it on your man's penis, you won't go far wrong.

However, some people are actually turned off by saliva, and if that's the case with either you or your partner, you'll have to use some alternative. Your own vaginal juices are ideal for this purpose: if you're flowing freely, you can just scoop them up on your fingertips and apply them to your man's shaft or glands.

But being realistic, most women can't rely on producing enough love juice to lubricate their man's organ thoroughly. That's why *artificial* lubricants are so widely sold these days. Among the popular ones are:

SEX PLAY

67

- Baby oil.
- Vaseline (petroleum jelly).
- K-Y Jelly.
- Moisturiser.
- Intensive Care (widely used in the USA).
- Astroglide (ditto).
- Talcum powder.
- Sun cream.
- Wet – a brand which has recently become popular in the UK.

You can buy all sorts of jolly lubricants with exotic colours and/or fragrances from sex shops – or by mail order. And if you'd feel embarrassed about going to a sex shop, you can simply use any bland and nice-feeling hand or face cream.

Two words of warning, though:

1   DON'T apply *oil-based* lubricants to your man's personal part if you're going to go on and use a condom. Oil-based products like Vaseline do unfortunately make holes in rubber!

2   Be a bit wary about using highly-perfumed or highly-coloured products, just in case they cause a *sensitivity reaction* in your guy – or yourself. Sensitivity reactions are typified by redness, soreness, itching and swelling. If one occurs, you should never use that product again.

PENIS TECHNIQUES: ASK HIM WHAT HE LIKES

OK, let's look at the caresses you can use on the penis of the man you love.

(Well, I hope you love him).

There's one tip to bear in mind before you start, and it's this. *Be guided by him.* I'm sure you know by now that you should tell him what YOU like when he's caressing your vulva. Well, in just the same way, you need to consult him about his feelings while you're rubbing or stroking his cock.

After all, remember that he has almost certainly been stroking that particular organ himself since about the age of thirteen! By now, he knows exactly which pressures feel good – and which ones don't.

So don't hesitate to keep saying things like 'Is that nice?' or 'Do you want me to press harder, darling?' and so on. Unfortunately, many couples go in for this kind of sex play in an embarrassed silence, which is quite crazy; after all, you can't be expected to use telepathy to find out which way your man wants his prick rubbed.

One other hint before we embark on specific penis-stimulating techniques: for most males (though not all) it's a terrific turn-on if you 'talk rude' to him while you're frigging his organ. Therefore, you'll probably achieve the best results if you keep making helpfully erotic remarks like 'What a marvellous cock!' and 'Darling, it's ENORMOUS…' Men just love to be told this type of thing – even if it isn't entirely true!

Furthermore, naughty sex play chat of this type is usually of great assistance to the many men who have some difficulty in getting an erection.

THE COCKTAIL SHAKER (SLOW AND FAST)

The basic penis caress is called 'the cocktail shaker', and you can see it demonstrated very frankly in the illustration on this page. All you do is to wrap your hand around your man's erect cock – preferably having first lubricated it with saliva or love-juice – and then move your fist up and down as indicated by the double arrow. Most men find this very exciting.

By the way, don't hesitate to press hard – it's extremely unlikely that you'll hurt your man (and he'll pretty soon tell you if you do!) Failure to press firmly enough is a very common error; it simply doesn't give the bloke enough stimulus.

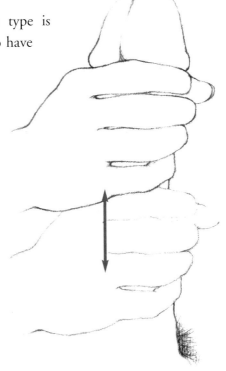

the
cocktail
shaker

You can do the cocktail shaker either slowly or fast, depending on how you and your man feel at the time. Slow, up and down movements can be very effective, particularly if you vary the power of your squeeze. But there are many times when it's good to go for a very fast rub up, aiming for about 30 strokes in 5 seconds – or about 350 per minute. Unlikely though that figure may sound, it's actually very easy for a lady with enthusiasm and nimble hands!

You'll have noticed that I began by saying that the cocktail shaker should be applied to the erect penis. In fact, it may not work terribly well if your man HASN'T got an erection and you're trying to give him one. Our next hand technique is far better for giving a chap a stiffy.

PLAYING THE OBOE

The method which I call 'Playing the Oboe' is shown in the illustration here. It's extraordinarily effective in helping a limp penis to get erect – and it's also very good to use on a cock which is already stiff.

As you can see, what you do is to put your thumb on the belly side of his prick (that's the side which is nearest to his tummy when he's erect). You then put your remaining fingers on the *other* side of his shaft.

It doesn't matter how many fingers you use for this, and you and he may find it intriguing to vary the number – sometimes taking his cock between your thumb and forefinger, sometimes using the middle finger as well, and sometimes adding the ring finger and even your little finger too.

The important thing is that you squeeze his shaft very firmly between your thumb and the other fingers (no, you won't damage him!). Then you move your hand up and down very rapidly.

While you do this, you may be able to feel,

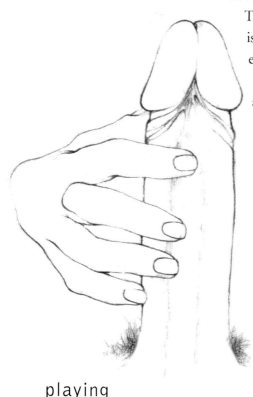

playing
the
oboe

between your fingertips, the internal cylinders which make up the shaft of his organ. And as you continue the up and down movement, you'll sense that the magic of your fingers is making blood flow into the cylinders and stiffen them, so that his penis will throb into full erection.

Incidentally, this is a VERY sexy technique. So unless you actually *want* him to come, do take it a bit easy once you've got his prick looking as though it's bursting at the seams! If you go on too intensively you may well push him over the brink.

THE REVERSE OBOE

This is exactly like the oboe technique except that your hand is reversed – in other words, your thumb is on the curved or heart side of his shaft, while your fingers are on the belly side. Naturally, it's easier to do this if you're facing him, for instance if you're kneeling on the bed or on the floor, between his knees.

Incidentally, the reverse oboe is just as good at summoning up a quick erection as the ordinary oboe. So it's well worth using if your guy sometimes has a bit of trouble getting lead in his pencil.

SIDE BY SIDE

The Side By Side method of getting your man going is shown in the illustration overleaf. This technique is very helpful if he's one of the many guys who have a slight problem in getting stiff. But it's also a nice caress to give your male.

In the previous caresses, you've been pressing on the front and back of the penis. But now, you're going to exercise your digital talents on the SIDES of his organ.

So, put the pad of your thumb against one side of his cock; place the pads of two of your fingers (normally the index and middle ones) against the other; squeeze quite firmly so that you can feel your thumb and finger almost meeting in the middle.

Now, keeping your wrist nice and relaxed, start moving your hand up and down very quickly With practice, you'll be able to do this well over 100 times a minute! In the case of a man who has trouble with his potency, you may have to keep this up for 10 minutes or more before he gets a good erection. I have to warn you that this is really TIRING until you get used to it. It's not a bad idea to take frequent rests, during which you suck or lick him.

side by side

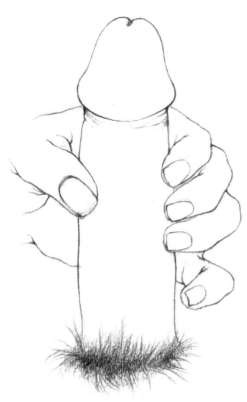

If you use this exciting Side By Side caress on a bloke who's already got a fine, full erection, you may actually make him come rather sooner than you think. So be guided by him as to how long to keep it up.

THE PALM ROLL

The 'Palm Roll' is shown in the illustration on the opposite page. It'll give your man interesting sensations which are quite different from those induced by the previous caresses.

This one works best if he's already erect, or at least partly erect. Hold his cock between the palms of your two hands, with your fingers straight and more or less together, as in the drawing.

Now simply ROLL his penis vigorously between your two hands, by moving one hand forward and the other one backward – and then repeating as many times as you like. If you're wearing any sharp rings, perhaps you'd better remove them first.

This nice caress – which works much better if your hands are oiled – is very easy to master. But if you feel at all uncertain before doing it for the first time, you can always practise on a bar of wet soap in your bath…

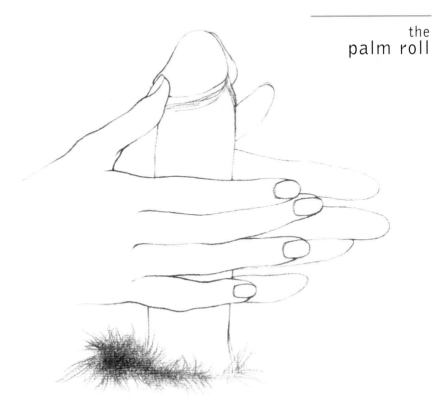

the
palm roll

THE HEART CARESS

You may remember from our chapter on male sexual anatomy that on the curved side of your man's penis is a little area which looks like an upside-down heart. If you're not sure where I mean, have a look at page 15.

This area is terrifically sensitive when a guy is erect. So a good thing to do to him when he's stiff is simply to lick your fingertip and – just like the lady in the drawing overleaf – rub the moistened finger pad to and fro across the heart. Alternatively, move your fingertip round and round. *Note: neither trick will work if he's not erect.*

All of this should give him intense pleasure. Indeed, you may well find that his cock twitches back quite dramatically when you touch him in this super-sensitive area (which is also one of the main targets in *oral* sex play – see Chapter Six). Do not be alarmed by this twitch; he will love it!

As a pleasant variation on the heart caress, try flicking your moist finger pad across the *string* – the little thread of tissue which runs vertically down from the

SEX PLAY

the **heart**
caress

heart to the shaft. It becomes very tight when your man is stiff, and some women acquire the skill of gently twanging it like someone playing a violin *pizzicato*.

THE PLEASURE RIDGE STROKER

As we saw in Chapter One, the erect male has a prominent ridge running straight down the curved side of his penis. I call this the pleasure ridge, for reasons which will be obvious in a moment.

In order to stimulate it, what do you do? First have a look at the illustration below, which shows a stiff male *zizi* with a fairly bursting pleasure ridge – along which a lady is running her fingertip.

Well, all you have to do is do the same. It may be a help if you moisten your fingertips first, or dust them with talcum powder. Then rub them firmly up and down the ridge, noticing the agreeable throbbing that this produces. You may find it helpful to hold the head of his cock steady with your other hand.

If you decide to go as far as making your man come this way, you may well be able to feel the surges of orgasm being transmitted through the pleasure ridge to your fingertips.

Note: this caress only works on the erect or semi-erect penis. So unlike some of the other techniques in this chapter, it isn't really much use as a treatment for impotence.

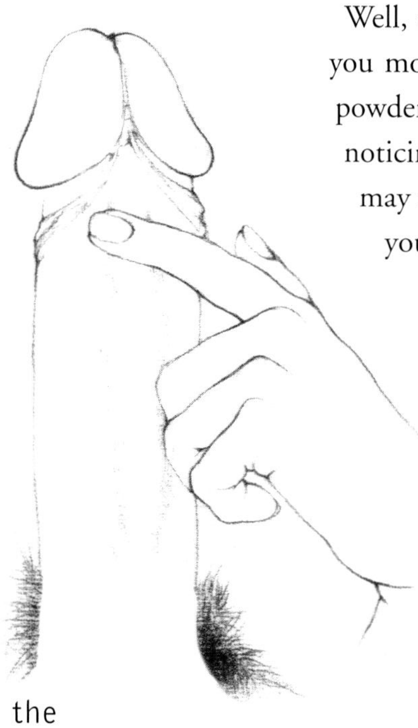

the
**pleasure
ridge** stroker

THE DOUBLE WHAMMY

This is a two-handed caress which will give your man very nice sensations. Like the previous technique, it won't work on the non-erect cock; your man has to have a good, taut erection before you can use it on him. Therefore, don't use this one if you're looking for help with a potency problem.

First, make sure that your nails are reasonably short and free of jagged edges; this is NOT, I'm afraid, a method for the lady with long, sharp nails – no matter how beautiful they look! Trying the double whammy with long nails would HURT.

Position yourself so that you're facing the same way as your bloke, and put your two thumbs on the belly side of his prick. Now, reach round with the fingers of both hands so your fingertips are touching the curved or heart side of his organ.

Next, align the POINTS of your fingers along the length of the penis – just like the illustration here. You'll note that the lady in the drawing has her fingertips on

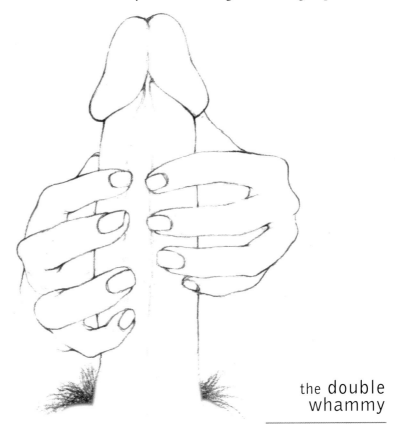

the double
whammy

either SIDE of the pleasure ridge. In fact, there's a very slight trough on either side of this ridge. Dig the points of your fingers into it.

Now all you have to do is to wiggle them up and down a little bit. This will augment your bloke's erection and give him some very nice feelings.

THE MALE U-SPOT CARESS

As we discovered in previous chapters, someone in an American university has recently come up with a new *female* erogenous zone: the U-spot, which is supposed to be located around a lady's urinary opening.

Well, it is possible to touch up the equivalent area in a male. However, the male urinary opening does have pain receptors in it as well as pleasure ones. Also, many guys tend to be very sensitive about it and they may – not unreasonably – be frightened about having it touched. So before you try this one, talk it over with your man – and when you're doing it, please take things easy.

Right: the male *urinary* opening is of course the little slit right at the tip of your man's penis. (Why people call it 'the urinary opening' I don't know – because of course it's also the opening for when his 'cum' comes spurting out.)

All you do is to pop a little dab of some bland cream or lubricant – your vaginal juices will do fine – on the tip of your forefinger and then, just like the woman in the illustration, rub it round and round the tip of his erect penis. Er… that's about it, really! I don't think it'll bring him to orgasm, but with luck he'll find it interesting and unusual.

Warning: under no circumstances should you poke any objects inside his urinary opening. I have seen some real disasters occur this way.

the
u-spot
caress

THE SPRINGBACK

This is a simple, fun caress to use on your man's erect penis. Do warn him what you're going to do first, won't you?

Sitting beside him on the bed (or wherever you happen to be), take his cock in your hand and gradually pull it down until it's nearly pointing at his feet. Obviously, if he feels any pain – which is unlikely – do stop.

Now simply let him go, like letting go of a bowstring. His organ will come twanging back up towards his belly. Repeat half a dozen times – but only if he liked it the first time.

As a variation, hold something soft and caressing (like a feather duster or a furry glove) where the head of his penis will brush against it when it springs back towards his tummy.

The springback works particularly well if you're taking a bath or shower together, when everything is nice and warm and soapy. Indeed, some couples have been known to use this method as a way of flicking the soap across the Jacuzzi…

THE MILKY WAY

Following on from what we've just said about soap, it's often a good idea to use something really frothy and jolly on your man's organ. This is good fun for both of you, and also makes it a lot easier to massage him.

Whipped cream is ideal for this job, but alternatively something like hair mousse will do very well. Just put dollops and dollops of it on your guy's cock, as in the illustration shown here – and then massage in well.

Incidentally, this is a good way of getting a bloke to erection if he's having a little difficulty You can combine it with sucking (see Chapter Six), provided of course that the foam you've used is edible.

the
milky way

Warning: please don't put on any foam which wasn't designed to come into contact with the human body. Edible things and preparations for the hair and skin are usually fine. But if either of you develops any soreness, stop at once – and don't use the stuff again.

the
cli-cli
caress

THE CLI-CLI CARESS

This is a simple and nice thing to do while you're rubbing your man's penis. Once it's erect, just bring the head of it towards you with your hand, and nuzzle the tip against your clitoris – as shown in the illustration here. This is exciting for him, as well as giving YOU lots of stimulation. In fact, it makes a lot of women come. It's often a good idea to let your love juices run on to his shaft while you're doing this, so as to provide lubrication for your hand movements.

FORESKIN TECHNIQUES

A French surgeon recently said that he was amazed by the attitude which British, American and Australian people take towards the foreskin of the penis. 'They seem to regard it as a rather unnecessary appendage,' he said. 'In contrast, we continentals see it as a source of fun, and love to play with it.'

I must say that that seems a very sensible attitude, since your man's foreskin (assuming he still has one) is packed with erotic nerve-endings – which is exactly what you'd expect, seeing that this is quite a large chunk of the skin of the most erotic organ in his body.

THE SKIN GAME

This is our first foreskin technique, although it is possible to do it even if your partner is circumcised. It's a very sensuous technique, and it's shown in the illustration opposite.

Here's what you do. First, lubricate his prick with some nice substance. Next, bring it to erection, if you haven't already done so. Now grasp it in the PALM of your hand, near the top. Take a fairly firm grip – and then slide your hand all the way down to the bottom of it, *taking all the loose skin with you.*

Your hand is now wrapped round the base of his penis, holding the skin tightly. This means that ABOVE your hand, all the remaining skin on his shaft is stretched very tightly indeed! That produces very intense feelings in the tautly straining shaft-skin.

the
skin
game

For a final touch, you use the fingers of your other hand to stroke, tease and tantalize that exquisitely stretched skin half-way up his shaft. Mmm… mmm!

THE PULLOVER

For this one, your man *does* need to have a foreskin. So if he's circumcised, forget it!

Start when he's not erect, and gradually pull his foreskin between your fingers as shown in the illustration over the page – as if you were trying to hide the head of his penis in the bottom of a paper bag.

Now all you need to do is to toy with the edges of the foreskin between your finger and thumb, rolling it over a little bit and keeping it taut. Meanwhile, encourage him with little kisses and licks, and a good erection should soon develop.

Obviously, when it *does* develop you'll have to let go of his foreskin – as the head of his penis sort of comes up out of the paper bag!

As a result, this tends to be a rather short-lived caress. Nonetheless, it's a good one

– particularly for helping men who need something a little out of the ordinary to help them get an erection.

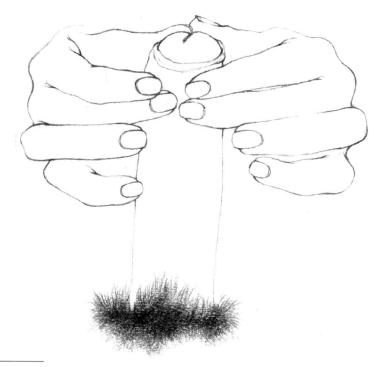

the
pullover

THE HÄAGEN-DAZS FILLER

This is a thoroughly daft game which you and your lover might like to play one night when you're both in the mood for a spot of pretty wacky fun.

First buy some Häagen-Dazs ice cream which, as you probably know, has strong romantic overtones. Put a carton of it by the bed.

Next, check that your man's penis isn't erect. Then draw his foreskin forward exactly as you did in our previous technique. And once you've made that little 'paper bag' effect, pop a little melting Häagen-Dazs inside it. Most men will like the rather agreeable and cool feeling on the head of the organ.

What you do next with the ice cream is up to you…

GINGER AND PEPPERMINT

In much the same way, you can put a little stem ginger or peppermint massage lotion inside your man's foreskin – provided he's agreeable, of course! Both of them can give him an agreeable angle.

Even if he hasn't got a foreskin, it's well worth buying some nice peppermint massage lotion from a pharmacy and sensuously rubbing this into his organ. Quite surprisingly, peppermint produces much the same agreeable tingly feeling in the sex organs as it does in the mouth.

Warning: on no account decide to use neat ginger or peppermint essential oil on your man's penis as they will cause a severe burning sensation. If anything you do apply to his penis causes redness, soreness or itching, this could be a sensitivity reaction – so don't use it again.

TESTICLE TECHNIQUES

Men are very, very wary indeed about having anything done to their testicles – and with good reason.

However, it is certainly worth your while caressing your man's balls, which are of course contained in the little pouch called his scrotum.

But don't expect to give him ORGASMS from doing this kind of thing. Remember that his scrotum is the exact anatomical equivalent of your outer lips; so you'll readily understand that caressing it is pleasant, but (just like caressing your outer labia) isn't going to fire off any climaxes.

THE STROKE

Having said that, plain ordinary *stroking* of his scrotum is nice for him. Run the tips of your fingers along the little horizontal wrinkles, and also down the vertical seam which is shown in the illustration on page 18, back in Chapter One.

Stroking the testicles themselves is OK too, as long as you don't expect some wonderfully explosive reaction from him. Many women also like to cradle either one ball or two in their hands and gently jog them up and down. But if he gets nervous – as some guys do – you'd better stop!

SEX PLAY

81

THE INDIAN TICKLER

You may remember from Chapter One that there's a curiously sensitive little triangle of SMOOTHER skin at the back of a man's scrotum – behind the wrinkled bit. You can see what I mean from the illustration on page 18 that you've just been looking at.

Well, it's quite simple to stimulate this little triangle. Just moisten a fingertip, slip it under his balls – like the Indian lady is doing in the illustration here – and tickle away… That's all there is to it!

the
indian
tickler

THE PULLDOWN

The pulldown is a simple technique used by topless massage girls who have found that it increases a man's pleasure. You do it while you are rubbing his penis with one hand.

Simultaneously, cup his whole scrotum in your other hand, and softly draw it downwards. This increases the pull on his cock and so intensifies the sensations for him.

The probable reason why topless massage parlours use it is that it often speeds up the orgasm and thus increases the throughput of customers! So take it a bit easy, unless you actually want him to come.

THE PERINEAL PLEASER

Your man's perineum is – as we explained in Chapter One – that little bit of ultra-sensitive skin which lies behind his scrotum, and in front of his bottom. As you probably know, touching a man there unexpectedly can make him leap into the air.

But during sex play, it's quite a nice area to stroke with your fingertips, or even prod quite deeply – because that deep pressure stimulates sexual areas located below his prostate gland.

Stroking the perineum is quite a good way to get your man interested in making love to you if he's feeling sleepy or lazy. It's also a good thing to do with your left hand while you're doing other equally pleasant things to him with your right one.

Note: his perineum like yours – is very near his anus. Don't stray into that particular area with your fingers until you've read all the warnings in Chapters Eleven and Twelve.

PREMATURE EJACULATION TECHNIQUE

Huge numbers of men come a bit too soon – or sometimes a lot too soon. This can cause them and their partners anything from mild frustration to deep despair. Indeed, it has ruined many a marriage. If your man suffers from severe premature ejaculation, he needs to see a doctor or psychologist who is well versed in the famous Masters and Johnson techniques of curing the condition. There is also mow a drug treatment available.

THE SQUEEZER

Those techniques are mainly based on a simple manoeuvre which the man's partner carries out with her hands. So if your guy's tendency to come a bit soon is only very mild, then you can help him yourself by using this manoeuvre on him.

It's called The Squeezer because it 'turns off' the urge to climax – just like that!

Have a look at the illustration on the next page and I'll explain what to do. The best thing is to sit or kneel down on the bed in front of him, so you're facing each other totally naked.

With your right hand, start to rub him up, using any of the basic techniques described in this chapter, such as the notorious Reverse Oboe.

Now… as soon as he says that he's feeling the urge to have an orgasm, immediately apply the special GRIP shown in the illustration. Note that your thumb-pad must be on the curved side of his penis – just over the heart region.

Similarly, your forefinger and middle finger must be on the belly side of his cock, with the forefinger just above the ridge and the middle finger below it.

The moment you've got your fingers in place, *squeeze them together hard*.

SEX PLAY

This does NOT hurt – but it takes away the desire to come. As soon as your bloke has calmed down a trifle, you can start happily rubbing his prick again and getting him excited. But as soon as he says 'I'm getting near to coming again', *apply the Squeezer once more.*

Doing this a dozen or even twenty times in an evening will gradually train your man to last much longer over a period of months – and eventually you'll be able to forget about the squeeze manoeuvre altogether. Thanks to this method, some men have increased their 'lasting time' from about five seconds to about forty-five minutes!

Note: if you go to a doctor or other therapist, our illustration will still be helpful to you, because accurate pictures of the squeeze manoeuvre aren't easy to find.

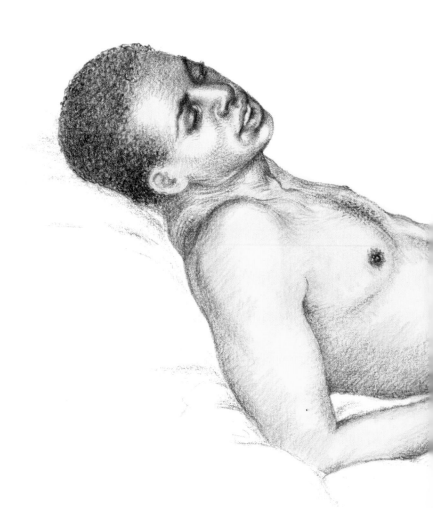

the **squeezer**

ORAL TECHNIQUES FOR A MAN TO USE ON A WOMAN

CUNNILINGUS

Cunnilingus, as you doubtless know, is not an Irish airline: it's actually a very effective (and generally much appreciated) way of doing nice things for your partner with your mouth.

Even today, some poor souls get themselves very upset about it, and say that it's 'wrong' or 'dirty'. That's nonsense, of course; there's nothing in the least unhygienic about cunnilingus. And how could there be anything 'wrong' about giving pleasure to the person you love?

Incidentally, the pleasure in question can be pretty intense – which is one reason for cunnilingus's great popularity with women. These days, most younger females (and many older ones!) do expect a guy to provide it as part of his range of love-making skills. Admittedly, they may not want it on every occasion – especially if the weather's chilly. As we'll see in a minute, the climate does tend to have a rather dramatic effect on the incidence of cunnilingus; it's quite difficult to do when you're perishing cold!

But what exactly is it? And how do you pronounce it?

Well, it comes from the old English word 'cunt' and the Latin word for 'tongue' – so literally, it means 'putting the tongue on the cunt'. But in fact, it covers pretty well *anything* you do with your mouth to your partner's vulva or vagina. Some authorities define it as 'the use of the lips, tongue or teeth on the female organ' – though personally I would NOT recommend employing your teeth! If you don't judge things right, you could give her a nasty nip.

How do you pronounce it? That's something which – I know from personal experience – gives many patients some embarrassment. There are three ways of saying the word, all of which are equally correct:

- 'Kunny – ling – us'.
- 'Koony – ling – us'.
- 'Kyoony – ling – us'.

Slightly bizarrely, some books refer to cunnilingus as 'cunnilinctus' – which does sound rather more like a cough mixture, doesn't it?

Other expressions which are often used to mean the same thing include the two French terms 'doing *Mimi*' and 'doing *Minette*', and the common American phrases 'going down on a woman', 'giving head to a woman', and also 'eating'.

AN ACQUIRED TASTE

Now, if you've never tried cunnilingus before, or have very little experience of it, I have to tell you that it is an acquired taste – in more than one sense.

Not all men are happy doing it, particularly if they've got some misguided notion that the female sex organ is dirty (it's a good deal cleaner than your hands or face, I can tell you!)

Also, the fact is that some guys are a bit *afraid* of the vagina and are reluctant to get too closely involved with it. But for the average chap who has a healthy interest in sex and a keen desire to please his woman, cunnilingus soon becomes great fun. Nevertheless, in the early days you may feel rather taken aback – or even disorientated – when you find a lady thrusting this extraordinary and rather strange-tasting organ into your face.

But persevere – and you will learn to enjoy it, especially as your skill with your lips and tongue begins to increase. That interesting feminine taste will cease to be in any way surprising or off-putting, and will in fact strike you as a real turn-on – especially when you realize that these exotic-tasting juices are flowing freely because of desire for YOU.

An experienced lover once said that kissing a moist vulva is like eating oysters or any other much-prized food: it tastes odd to start with, but soon you learn to love it. Personally, I'd compare a woman's cunny to a glass of wine: when a boy's lips first touch it, he's not sure he likes it – but, oh, how nice it becomes later…

One final point about that rather dramatic female taste. Even though you, as a man, may think it's great, it's as well to remember that your partner may NOT. For instance, a young man recently rang my wife's Agony Aunt TV programme in a terrible state of distress because his fiancée wouldn't kiss him any more.

Why? It eventually emerged that although she loved cunnilingus, she absolutely *hated* the taste of her own vagina on his lips and tongue afterwards.

If that's a problem in your relationship, then the answer is simply to wipe your mouth with a tissue after giving your lover head. However, in practice many women

SEX PLAY

tongue play

do rapidly become accustomed to this very special female taste on a man's lips – and indeed, I have to say that some of them are heavily turned on by it.

THE QUESTION OF SMELL

Closely linked to the question of taste is, of course, the question of smell. For some extraordinary reason, most books on sex don't talk about this subject at all, even though it's one which worries many men and women.

The fact is that the female love juices *do* smell. But they're supposed to do so; that's the way Nature designed things. Indeed, these love juices give off chemicals called pheromones (pronounced 'FEAR – o – moans') which are colossally powerful sexual attractants. They work at VERY low concentrations – so they attract the male even when he's not aware he's smelling them.

These pheromones are secreted by the sex organs of many members of the animal kingdom. For instance, the virgin empress moth manages to turn out a pheromone which attracts males at the almost unbelievable range of 6.75 miles (11 kilometres), according to the *Guinness Book of Records*!

On a slightly less record-breaking scale, it is thought that there are some women who produce a lot of pheromones in their vaginal secretions during day-to-day life – and not just when they're sexually excited. These women seem *to attract men without the men really knowing why.*

For instance, I remember a doctor who, as she freely admitted herself, was distinctly lacking in physical beauty. Yet at any party, young men swarmed around her without knowing why they found her so extraordinarily attractive. I believe that it was because she exuded vaginal pheromones; certainly, I could just detect a hint of an exotic gynaecological fragrance when I stood near her…

Back in the 1990's, an American firm started marketing an alleged love potion – a perfume which seems to mimic the aroma of vaginal secretions. It's called Athena Pheromone, and press reports describe it as 'attracting men to women like bees to honey'. Its developer, Ms Winnifred Cutler of Pennsylvania, claims that 'those wearing it are having and enjoying more sex than ever before'.

Well, whatever the merits of this particular pheromone – which is extremely expensive – the fact remains that the distinctive scents of the vagina are meant to be a turn-on for the human male. So if you are a human male, then the best thing to do is to enjoy them. Like the guy in the illustration on pages 90 - 91, just be happy that your partner is letting you put your tongue, lips and nose in her 'perfumed garden'.

COPING WITH PERIODS

Before we get down to the nitty-gritty of cunnilingus techniques, a brief word about your partner's periods. Even today, most women do feel quite embarrassed about the subject of menstruation. Many of them feel that they smell bad during a period (though curiously enough, this smell isn't detectable to the average guy). So you'll probably find that your lover doesn't want you to go down on her while she has 'the curse'.

On the other hand, there are some very raunchy women who are more than keen to go in for sex play at this time of the month – especially if, as is quite common, they've discovered that having a climax eases period pain and relieves tension.

And if you're happy to touch up your partner's clitoris with your tongue, there's no reason at all why you shouldn't do so. But I'd like to suggest to any women who are reading this chapter that if you want your man to go down on you during your menses, you should make sure that you are really well-plugged with a fresh tampon. Some women actually insert a contraceptive cap if they want to go in for cunnilingus at this time of the month.

THE DIFFICULTIES OF GETTING YOURSELF POSITIONED

Where cunnilingus is concerned, the biggest problem for many couples is simply getting themselves positioned right. You see, when a woman gives a man oral sex, getting in position ISN'T much of a problem; because of the simple fact that *his sex organs stick out*, all she has to do is to get her lips somewhere in front of his groin.

But as you've doubtless noticed, a lady's sex organs do not stick out; furthermore, they are hidden deep between her thighs. And it's between those thighs that you've got to put your head if you're going to give her pleasure.

I'd like female readers to appreciate the fact that it's not actually very easy for a man to get his head right down between the thighs. There isn't a lot of room – and there's often difficulty in managing to breathe! A male friend of mine once suggested that us guys should be equipped with a snorkel before attempting cunnilingus…

SEX PLAY

The average guy's response to all this is simple: he pushes the woman's legs wide apart, often leaning on her thighs with his hands so that her knees are splayed out sideways. But what Joe Average doesn't realize is that, very often, this position is extremely uncomfortable for a woman! Furthermore, a lot of females simply *cannot* come in that posture.

Miss Tuppy Owens, the famous author of *The Sex Maniac's Diary*, talks a lot of good sense about cunnilingus, and she speaks with some feeling about unfortunate experiences she has had with men who are 'insensitive' about ensuring that the female is in a comfortable position. She says: 'Most men think we should lie on our backs with our legs apart, and that might not be the position we want to be in. They pin our knees aside, and even rest their elbows on them for comfort!' She also points out that there are some women who cannot climax when lying on their backs – so giving them oral sex while they're supine on the bed may be quite nice for them, but won't bring them to orgasm.

My advice, for what it's worth, is to ASK your partner how she'd like to be positioned – rather than plonking her down in whatever posture YOU think is suitable. However, do make clear to her that you have to be reasonably comfortable too – and that you have to be able to draw breath!

For many couples, these positions work out well:

- The woman sits naked on a chair with her knees about 12 inches (30 cm) apart, while her man kneels in front of her.
- She stands upright with her feet about 18 inches (45 cm) apart; again, he kneels in front of her.
- She lies on her back on the top half of the bed with her legs comfortably parted; he lies on his chest between her knees.
- She's on her back as above – but this time he's lying beside her, with his feet up near the pillows and his head at the level of her groin (but this position will only give you limited access to her vagina).
- He's lying flat on his back, and she's kneeling astride his face.
- She's lying with her legs dangling over the edge of the bed, and he's kneeling on the floor with his mouth on her cunny.

Incidentally, do be prepared to change your position quite frequently – especially if she says that she doesn't think she can climax in the one you're using.

KEEP HER WARM WHILE YOU'RE DOING IT

There is one big drawback to almost every cunnilingus position, and it's this. *You can get freezing cold!*

I'm not joking: one reason why the northern races of the world – such as the British, the Canadians and the Nordic peoples – have never had a great reputation as practitioners of tonguing is the fact that you can freeze to death doing cunnilingus in a chilly bedroom.

With fellatio (oral sex given by a woman to a man) the situation is quite different. For instance, in Glasgow or Aberdeen young Donald can simply unzip his trousers, or indeed lift his kilt, and Bonny Mary of Argyll can cheerfully fasten her lips round his penis *while both of them remain fully dressed.*

In stark contrast, cunnilingus is very difficult to do unless the lady has stripped off, though I suppose she could keep her woolly vest on! She has to be virtually naked below the waist. Potential result in a northern clime: double pneumonia.

Now you may say that a couple can always go in for cunnilingus under the protection of warm blankets or a duvet. But in actual fact, it is not at all easy for a chap to provide satisfactory tonguing when his head is buried under heavy bedclothes. Quite seriously, he can almost asphyxiate down there – and furthermore, he can't see what on earth he's supposed to be doing to his partner, unless he carries a lamp.

What all this is leading up to is one simple piece of advice. If you want to give your partner good cunnilingus, dispense with bedclothes and do it uncovered – *but for heaven's sake do it in a really warm room.*

Don't attempt it below 72°F (22°C)! If you haven't got central heating, then invest in a really good fan heater for your bedroom. And consider switching it on a good half-hour before you invite her to gambol naked on the sheets with you.

SEX PLAY

GETTING STARTED

OK, now you're nearly ready to get started. But before you fling yourself wildly on to your lover's cli-cli with lust-crazed eyes, could I just remind you that in cunnilingus (as, indeed, in all sex play activities) there are certain things which you must keep firmly in mind from the outset. They are:

- Romance.
- Preliminary cuddling.
- Laughter.
- Tenderness.

So do NOT just say to your partner 'I'm going to do cunnilingus on you tonight, dear' – and then launch yourself at her groin. Most women will find this stormtrooper approach to oral sex distinctly off-putting, to say the least...

Therefore, having made sure that she's warm and comfortable – as indicated above – do for heaven's sake kick off by doing common sense things like kissing her and cuddling her and telling her she's lovely.

Next, do give her some idea of what sort of act you're about to perform on her fair body! As you can imagine, having a bloke suddenly fasten his lips on your clitoris can be an unnerving business, especially if you're a lady who's a trifle inexperienced in these matters.

You don't actually have to *say* that you'd like to go down on her if you don't want to; it's sufficient to make your intentions clear by gradually working your way down her body – taking plenty of time to kiss and nibble her breasts and belly. Try to nuzzle the skin of her lower belly UPWARDS, as this puts a stretch on her clitoris.

The essence of success is to take things gradually. Don't rush her! If in doubt, try to spend several minutes on kissing and tonguing her pubic hair and her thighs before you start making any serious approach to her vulva.

Mind you, if (like many women these days) she simply grabs your head at an early stage in the proceedings and presses your face straight into her moist cunny, then I think you can take it that you have her permission to proceed pretty quickly... Nevertheless, her clitoris should NOT usually be your initial target – because it is such a sensitive, and sometimes over-sensitive, little organ. It's better to begin around the exotic fringes of the vulva, as I'll explain in a moment.

KISSING AND LICKING AND SUCKING

But first, let's get ourselves clear about what you're supposed to be doing to her vulva during oral sex. The main things are:

- Kissing.
- Licking.
- Sucking.

Do not blow – for reasons explained in the Health Warning section at the end of this chapter. And in my view, it's unwise to go in for biting; after all, how would you like somebody snapping their teeth together round your delicate personal parts?

In addition to licking and kissing and sucking, do all the tender nuzzling and nudging that you can. You may be surprised to hear that your nose, cheeks, forehead and chin can play quite a substantial role in giving your partner the pleasure she wants.

Above all, do what she asks you to do! For many women, the ideal is to provide a sort of moist, romantic fusion between her lover's lips and her own sex organ. If you achieve this, you'll be doing well. Very well.

WORKING ON HER OUTER LIPS

So, let's assume that you've been kissing around her pubic hair and her inner thighs for a few minutes, and you decide that it's time to go for her vulva. What do you do next?

Well, unless she tells you differently, it's not a bad idea to begin by just applying gentle, loving kisses to her outer lips.

In case you don't remember, these are the two plump, hairy lips which lie on either side of the vulva. They're pretty sexually sensitive, even though you're not likely to induce an orgasm by kissing them. But planting your lips on them is a nice, tender thing to do – and it's not in any way threatening, as a sudden stab at the clitoris can be!

SEX PLAY

So, kiss, lick, and suck those outer lips, enjoying their flavour as you do so. (Did you know that women have *different* flavours? If I tell you that redheads are usually the tangiest, I hope that you won't be tempted to play away from your partner in order to check out this observation.)

If you're not sure what to do next and your lover isn't giving you any particular instructions about what she wants, then quite an entertaining thing to do for her is just to run your tongue up and down the little groove which runs vertically between her inner and her outer lips. If you're not sure what I mean, go back and have a quick look at the illustration on page 23. I'm sure she won't mind…

WORKING ON HER INNER LIPS

By now, her *inner* lips should be looking perky, pink and moist. And if by any chance they're not all that moist, then use your mouth to make them so.

Now run your tongue-tip up and down them. Suck softly on each lip in turn. And with pursed lips, push them gradually out sideways – so stretching the S-zone a little – just like the guy in the illustration is doing.

lips
on lips

If you haven't already done so; now is a good time to bring your *hands* into the action too. For instance, while you're kissing her right inner lip and pressing it outwards, you can be using your right forefinger to stretch her other lip in the opposite direction. Indeed, you can use almost any of the finger-stretch techniques described back in Chapter Three, while your mouth is busy with her inner lips.

And it may well be that your partner will want to join in herself at this stage, stroking her own clitoris or whatever. The more that the two of you can co-operate, the better.

WORKING ON HER OPENING

I think it's fair to say that the aim of most cunnilingus is to finish up by concentrating on your loved one's clitoris. However, there are other things you can do along the way if you (and she) wish.

One of them is simply to apply your lips to her vaginal opening. To do this, you use your two hands to spread her inner and outer lips apart; in between, you can see the ending gap that leads into her vagina. Just move your head forward, purse your lips and apply them to it.

Now work your mouth around in that opening, trying to assess what gives her most pleasure. Don't neglect to put your tongue-tip on her U-zone – which, as you'll see if you go back to the drawing on page 23, is the area round the little bud of her urinary opening. This will give her intriguing and – I hope – nice sensations.

WHAT YOUR NOSE DOES!

While you're passing her vaginal opening, or indeed anywhere else in the lower part of her vulva, you'll very likely find that your nose is bumping around the region of her clitoris – that is, assuming you are *facing* her and are not head down.

It's perfectly OK for your nose to do this, because the gentle nuzzling gives her added clitoral stimulation. However, if you have any nose infection, you definitely shouldn't be doing cunnilingus at all – see the Health Warning at the end of the chapter.

SEX PLAY

WORKING ON HER CLITORIS

When she's ready, you can move on to applying your lips to her clitoris – though it may be best to work a little to one side of it and just above it before you finally go for that tiny pink button.

What do you do to it?

Well, once again you kiss it, lick and suck it, varying what you're doing according to the degree of response and encouragement you get from her.

KISSING THE CLITORIS If you're a bit uncertain about this, a good trick is just to purse your lips and put them softly on her 'clitty'. Then let HER move her hips against your lips so as to get the pressures and feelings that she wants.

Alternatively, just touch your lips to her clitoris and then shake your head slightly from side to side, then nod it up and down. Take great care to keep varying the force which you're applying to her clit – though you may well find that if she gets really turned on, she may clutch your head against her with considerable power.

LICKING THE CLITORIS This is quite easy to do, and produces extremely intense sensations. Make sure your tongue-tip is wet, and then prod it sensuously all round her clitoris. You'll probably find there's one particular spot that really drives her mad – so lick enthusiastically at it.

But bear in mind that, two minutes later, that particular spot *may no longer be much of a turn-on for her*. In that case, let her direct you to somewhere else around the clitoris; even though it may only be a tiny distance away, it will feel quite different to her.

Another good approach to clitoris-licking is just sticking out your tongue and keeping it still. One female expert

tonguing
clitoris
from below

100

says: 'Most women love to sway their hips up and down, so that the clitoris rubs on an almost motionless tongue'. That's correct: this technique gives the lady absolute control of where she wants to be licked; of how fast; and of how firmly

Incidentally, there are two main ways of approaching the *cli-cli* with your tongue. Up till now, I've been assuming that you're doing it from BELOW your partner's clitoris, as in the drawing on page 100 – in other words, with you facing her. But you can also lick her clit from ABOVE, in the way shown in the drawing below. Frankly, access isn't so easy this way, but it is quite a convenient and natural thing to do when you've been kissing somewhere further up her body, such as her breasts or her tummy

SUCKING HER CLITORIS If she enjoys it, don't hesitate to suck on her clitoris. Most women find this very agreeable and exciting, though personally I don't think you should try it till she's reasonably well aroused. Having somebody sucking hard on your *kitzler* when you're not expecting it could come as a bit of a nasty shock.

Also, I'd recommend that you take care not to suck TOO HARD. It's probable that violent suction could lead to Delvin's Haematoma of the Clitoris – the condition I mentioned earlier in this book, in which a painful blood clot develops inside the organ.

tonguing
clitoris
from **above**

PUTTING YOUR TONGUE INSIDE

Let's forget about the clitoris for the moment, and switch to a very effective yet much under-used love-play technique: putting your tongue inside her vagina. Properly carried out, this will drive most women wild.

You remember how a few pages back I explained about how to put your lips over your loved one's vaginal opening? Well, we start from there.

So, you're lying or kneeling facing her, with your lips against the opening of her vagina. Now just thrust your moist tongue forward and in.

Though this won't dilate her S-for-stretch zone all that much (because the bulk of the tongue isn't very great compared with the bulk of a penis) she will very much appreciate the extraordinarily intimate sensation which this produces in her vagina.

Now try rolling your tongue around and moving it about, trying to judge her reactions to what you're doing. Admittedly, assessing her response may be a teeny bit difficult, since your eyes should be buried somewhere in her pubic hair! But if she makes noises of delight, you can be fairly sure you're doing the right thing.

putting your
**tongue
inside** her

As you can see from the drawing here, the average chap's tongue will *not* go very far into the vagina – only about 1 $\frac{1}{2}$ inches (just under 4 cm) in fact. So forget any ideas of getting up to the topmost part of her love tunnel.

Also, I think it's extremely unlikely that any man – except perhaps one with an astoundingly long tongue – could hope to reach the Famous Female G-spot with it. But you never know…

Finally, one very practical thing you can do with your tongue inside her vagina is simply this: *move it in and out.*

Obviously, here you're imitating the action of your penis during intercourse. So you'll give her some quite exotic sensations which are rather reminiscent of intercourse, but naturally rather different – not least because your tongue is so much smaller than your cock.

Incidentally, I must warn you that this last movement (in and out) is VERY tiring. It pulls on the muscles at the root of the tongue, so you may feel pain there and have to take frequent breaks.

Women in general do not know about the existence of the tongue pain, so if your partner hasn't read this chapter you may have to explain to her that it's no good shouting 'Don't stop! Don't stop!' at you when your tongue muscles are screaming for a rest…

MORE EXOTIC WAYS OF DOING CUNNILINGUS

When your partner is thoroughly happy about oral sex play, you can (if you both wish) move on to some rather more *outré* ways of doing it.

FROM BEHIND

For instance, try it from behind – like the couple shown in the drawing below. There are various ways of doing this, but a simple one is for the woman to get on all fours on the bed, and for her lover to lie or kneel behind her and touch her up with his tongue.

I would stress that this is a method that requires the female partner to have total confidence in her man. If you're not yet very used to each other, or if she has

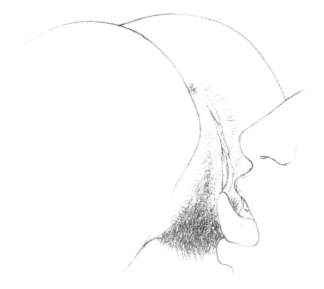

from **behind**

reservations about having her bottom exposed to your close-up view, then best forget it for a while.

Also, I have to admit that not all men are happy about this cunnilingus position. After all, you have got your nose practically up her *derrière* – which is not every chap's cup of tea! But stay with it, lads, and you could get to like it...

Ah, yes; a quick word about farting, since this is the position in which it's most likely to cause concern.

Many men and women go through agonies of embarrassment about the possibility of farting during oral sex. Some of them feel that their partners will be utterly disgusted, or even leave them, if they go and pass wind in bed.

But this is crazy. As international etiquette expert Drusilla Beyfus says, 'We all have bodies – and all our bodies produce wind.'

In fact, it is a truth *not* universally acknowledged that the normal, fit body produces over 3 $\frac{1}{2}$ pints (around 2 litres) of gas per day. And it has to come out!

Furthermore, it's quite inevitable that it will sometimes emerge during the wild abandon of oral sex play. If that happens what do you do?

Well, the best thing for *both* of you to do is simply to laugh – and carry on. If there is a smell (and in many cases there isn't – it depends which gases are contained in the wind), Miss Beyfus' advice is that the proper thing to say is 'So sorry' and then wave something like a hanky that will waft it all swiftly away.

Mind you, I think she was giving etiquette advice about afternoon tea at the Ritz, rather than cunnilingus...

THE 'SIT ON MY FACE' TECHNIQUE

This one is extremely popular in novels – or, at least, in the sort of novel where the heroine is willing to plonk herself on the hero's face at the drop of a knicker.

But in the real world, many couples are quite doubtful about trying this kind of thing. I recently asked a very experienced and sexually liberated female to jot down what she thought women felt about the posture. She wrote: 'Can be tremendously exciting with the right man. But not worth trying with someone who you don't love and trust. You can feel very undignified sitting up there on your own. You can also get very cold.'

Men too can have their doubts about this rather outrageous posture. Not every male is totally happy with having a damp vulva pinning his face down! And some guys are a bit worried about finding their noses jammed in between somebody's buttocks – no matter how exciting that somebody may be...

Still and all, there are lots of couples for whom an occasional bout of face-sitting is terrific fun. So if you both feel up to it, here's what you do.

The man must of course lie flat on his back – preferably with his lips moistened. The woman can either face:

- UP the bed (i.e. facing him) or
- DOWN the bed (i.e. facing his feet).

She should kneel down, straddling his head, and then gradually lower herself till her pussy is on his face. (Note for any women reading this chapter: make sure he can breathe.)

Women who really like this technique will then in effect use the man's face as a sort of live stimulation device, shifting and churning their hips so as to bring the clitoris – or whatever part of the vulva they want stimulated – into contact with the guy's lips or tongue or chin. If he is facing his lady, he can increase the stimulation by using his fingers as well.

In fact, having the woman face the man may well be preferable to having her face *away* – mainly because you can communicate a bit better. If she faces away from him, communication is virtually impossible, owing mainly to the fact that his eyes are buried somewhere in her bottom!

Though I've made this sitting-on-his-face posture sound a trifle wacky, there's no doubt that for some highly-sexed couples it's very thrilling. In particular, women who like being 'in control' have told me that they derive wonderful sensations from being able to press the moist vulva down so intimately on to the mouth of someone they love.

THE SOIXANTE-NEUF
Now, you can also do cunnilingus on your lover as part of the famous *soixante-neuf* (or 69) manoeuvre.

We'll be dealing with the famous 69 more fully in the next chapter. But if you're not totally sure what it is, then turn ahead and have a quick look at the illustration on page 130 - 131.

For the moment, let's just sort out what you should do if a woman asks you to give her the *soixante-neuf*. You can perform this either:

- On your sides, or
- With one of you on top of the other.

My personal view is that lying on your side is less of a physical strain for everyone, but there are certainly many couples who disagree with me, and who like doing it with either the guy or the gal on top. However, your partner may really dislike being trapped underneath you, so ASK her what she wants.

She is of course sucking or kissing your penis, and you will have your head in the general region of her vulva. The precise *level* of your head will depend very much on the difference between your heights – but in most cases you will wind up with your face very deep between her thighs, so that you are in fact gazing up her botty.

Basically, you have two jobs now:

- Don't get yourself stifled to death.
- Apply your mouth to her pussy in whatever way seems to turn her on most.

Licking her clitoris and putting your tongue inside her vagina are usually very effective. So too are pretty well any of the mouth-music techniques which I've described earlier in this chapter. And don't hesitate to use your fingers as well – or to use your hands to pat and squeeze her bottom, if that's what she likes.

One word of warning: don't get too many optimistic ideas about synchronizing orgasm while using the *soixante-neuf*. This can be quite difficult, partly because your heads are so far apart from each other. But some couples can achieve it, and when it happens it's very nice too. See Chapter Six for more info.

COMBINATION TECHNIQUES

No matter which cunnilingus caress you use to give your partner pleasure, please bear in mind that you can usually increase that pleasure by putting your fingers inside her at the same time – or by using your fingertips to stroke her clitoris or other parts of her pussy.

CUNNILINGUS PLUS FINGER CARESSES

The recent discovery that many women need simultaneous vaginal AND clitoral stimulation if they're to reach orgasm easily is important: it means that a skilled lover who's trying to bring his lady to climax with cunnilingus should generally consider using his hands as well.

For instance, he can touch up her 'clit' with his tongue-tip while using his first two fingers to stretch her S-zone and frig her vagina. Or he can put his tongue in her vagina and use his finger-pads on her clitoris. Double stimulation of this sort is often quite hard to resist!

CUNNILINGUS PLUS A VIBRATOR

In the same way, it's so often useful (and fun) to give your lover cunnilingus while touching her up with a vibrator – as long as you don't mind all that buzzing round your ears…

Vibrator techniques for use by a man are described in Chapter Seven. But if you've read what I've said above the importance of DOUBLE stimulation for many women, you'll see that very useful – and orgasm-inducing – combinations of cunnilingus and vibrator include:

- Touching up her clit with your tongue-tip while sensuously stretching her S-zone with a standard-shaped vibrator.
- Putting your tongue inside her while applying any kind of vibrator to her clitoral region and her inner and outer lips. And don't forget that it's probable that on some nights you could really blow her mind by combining cunnilingus with a vibrator AND your fingers – and very possibly her fingers as well.

SEX PLAY

COMBINING WITH RUDE FOOD

Once a couple have grown really used to each other and are happy to try slightly daft things together, it often becomes good fun to incorporate the use of sexy foods into oral sex play For some reason, this activity seems to drive old-fashioned moralists into a fury, but there we are.

The use of foods in fellatio is discussed in the next chapter. But how do we use foodstuffs in cunnilingus?

Simple. Ask her what foods she would like you to suck or munch from her body. Most women will go for things like creams, jellies and sauces. They may even opt for ice-cream, provided it's not too cold. And basically, all you have to do is to ladle the stuff erotically over her quim – and then cheerfully lick it up!

Men tend to fantasize about putting hard things, like carrots or courgettes (zucchini) half-way inside the vagina, and then nibbling them out. Well, OK. But you may find that your partner isn't quite as keen as you are on this – who knows?

One legendary rock star became famous for putting a Mars Bar inside his lady, and then spending the evening munching at it. But I'm not recommending this myself, because I feel there's a faint chance that putting such sweet things inside the vagina could trigger off an attack of the dreaded thrush (a.k.a. candida or monilia).

Also, do be careful not to put in anything which could break up and leave bits or crumbs inside. Foreign bodies in the vagina do cause a discharge if they're left there too long, I'm afraid. And it could be embarrassing going to a doctor to have a large chunk of Cadbury's Flake removed…

COMBINING WITH WINE

One of the great traditions of cunnilingus is combining it with wine. Back in Roman days, I understand it was quite common for a handsome emperor to pour a bottle of agreeable Tuscan plonk over his favourite concubine's vulva. And if you can afford it, a little occasional wine-play is certainly good fun for both partners. Naturally, you won't lash out on Veuve Clicquot for this purpose – except perhaps on special occasions such as your Diamond Wedding. But a glass of (say) Australian Cabernet-Sauvignon is no great expense, and both of you can have a good deal of amusement from it.

What do you do? First, make sure that whatever you're lying on isn't going to be stained by the wine. And agree that in the very unlikely event of the wine stinging the woman's vulva (personally, I have never known such a thing to happen) you'll stop immediately and wash it away.

Now the man should gradually pour a little wine into the lady's pubic hair, and begin to lick and suck it up. He continues doing this as it trickles down over her vulva – and naturally he should take care to pay special attention to her clitoris and any other spots which seem to be giving her pleasure.

There are all sorts of variations on wine-play which sensuous couples will enjoy. For instance, an uninhibited woman will sometimes take a glass of (say) Chablis in her own mouth – and then transfer it to her lover's mouth in a lingering kiss so that he can use it to moisten and tongue her vulva…

Forgive me if I nostalgically conclude this section with a question-and answer which appeared many years ago in my own advice column in the British woman's magazine SHE:

> Q. My husband is keen on wine, and the other night he asked me to try 'combining two great pleasures' by letting him kiss my most intimate area after first pouring on about half a glass of 1968 Burgundy. Do you approve?
>
> A. *No, I don't. After all, there are certain standards to be maintained in this age of fast slipping values, aren't there? The correct year would be a '66 or '67 – or indeed (dare I say it?) a '69.*

HEALTH WARNING

So, cunnilingus is good fun – and indeed, a great help to many women who have difficulty getting aroused or reaching orgasm. But here are a few snippets of common sense health guidance to bear in mind:

*   Don't try it if the man has any kind of mouth, nose or throat infection.
*   At all costs, do not do it if the man is suffering from a cold sore (*herpes labialis*) on his lip – this could give the woman a variety of herpes virus.

SEX PLAY

- Although cunnilingus carries practically no health risk for a man, it's probably better to avoid it if the woman has any vaginal infection.
- Throughout this book, I've assumed that I'm talking to couples in long term, stable relationships. But if you're NOT in a mutually faithful relationship, do bear in mind that there probably has been at least one case of HIV being transmitted (from woman to man) during cunnilingus.
- Though people often talk about BLOWING in connection with oral sex, *the man must not blow*. Why? Firstly, blowing will introduce mouth germs into the inner part of the woman's vagina, and perhaps higher up. I admit that most of the time this may not matter, but it could cause an infection. Much more seriously, blowing into the vagina may occasionally introduce air into the female's bloodstream. THIS CAN KILL. I well remember the case of a young British couple who liked going in for what's known in some parts of the UK as 'fanny farting' (*note to US readers*: in England, the fanny is the vulva, not the buttocks). This means blowing in air and letting it come out again. Tragically, one night the woman collapsed and died – killed by an air bubble in her circulation.
- Finally, could I ask male readers to remember that during oral sex play you have a unique opportunity to inspect your loved one's vulva and to *notice if anything's wrong healthwise*. You probably don't realize that women cannot see their own sex organ. So you have a much better view of it than she's ever had!

Urge her to go to the doctor if you ever notice any of the following:

- An unexplained lump. An unexplained raw place – even if it's painless.
- Tiny warts – these are very common and often unnoticed by the woman.
- Any unexplained bleeding or discharge.

Your vigilance could save her life.

6

ORAL
TECHNIQUES FOR
A WOMAN
TO USE ON A
MAN

FELLATIO

Yes, fellatio is what women do to fellers… though I have to admit that the word isn't really derived from 'fellow' at all. It comes from the Latin verb meaning 'suck'. Actually, fellatio doesn't just mean cock-sucking; it covers any activity in which the woman's mouth comes into contact with the guy's penis.

Do most women do it? Well, certainly, most younger females happily engage in it these days, and many more mature ones too – even though a generation or two back it was widely considered to be dirty, obscene or even perverted.

Of course, it's none of these things. Just in case you're worried about the 'dirt' aspect, let me reassure you: you're much more likely to catch germs from kissing a man's mouth than you are from kissing his penis.

As for being obscene or perverted – well, how could you use such words to describe such a tender and delightful way of giving happiness to the man you love?

And you will give him *intense* happiness. To be frank, men derive quite exquisite pleasure from being sucked by a woman. In fact, the sensations which you can produce with your mouth are so powerful that – as we'll see later in this chapter – one particular method of fellatio is an excellent treatment for mild impotence.

Incidentally, you may hear various different expressions which are used to describe doing fellatio on your man. They include:

- Fellating him.
- Giving him head.
- Going down on him.
- Sucking him off.
- Eating him.
- Giving him the *gemmarouche* or *gemma rouge* (terms allegedly derived from Arabic).
- Giving him a blow job.

This last expression is misleading and dangerous. As I'll explain in the Health Warning section at the end of this chapter, at all costs you must NOT blow!

fellatio

EMOTIONAL ASPECTS OF FELLATIO

Now, I don't know how you feel about fellatio but my experience has been that, emotionally speaking, women fall into three main groups:

- A small group who hate the whole idea, and who are really disgusted by the thought of putting their lips on a man's penis.
- A very large group who may have had a few doubts about fellatio at first (principally related to not being very sure what to do), but who rapidly decide that it's a nice, loving thing to do with their partners.
- A fairly small group who take to it with the most astonishing enthusiasm, and develop a real pride in how good they are at it!

If you're one of the first group, then the main thing I would say to you is this: *don't let yourself be pushed into it against your will*. Alas, men are awful about saying to women 'If you really loved me, you'd do such-and-such for me'. So don't give in to this kind of thing. If you don't like it, don't do it.

But what if you belong to the second group? Well, my advice is to *talk* to your partner about any slight doubts you may have, particularly over the question of coping with his orgasm (see later section). Also, talk to him about what he likes – so that you know you're doing what pleases him. And do for heavens' sake make YOUR feelings known to him! If there's some aspect of fellatio which you don't fancy (for instance, violent thrusting by the male – a very common feminine dislike) then please do tell him that you're not going to put up with it. After all, it's your mouth…

If you're in the third group of women – the ones who absolutely *love* going down on their partners – then good luck to you. In this chapter, you'll find various techniques which I think will be new to you, and which I very much hope you'll enjoy using with your man.

THINGS THAT PUT WOMEN OFF

If your man hasn't read this section, I suggest you *insist* that he does. There are three things which may bother the average woman about fellatio, and men ought to be aware of them. They are as follows:

- Women are easily – and most understandably – put off by the sight or taste of a cock which hasn't been properly washed. For some reason, this simple statement is regarded by some males as offensive! (I have noticed that *male* magazine editors, as opposed to female ones, tend to try to censor it if I put it in print.) But us guys do need to wash ourselves once or more per day – and I do assure you that it is the height of bad form to ask a lady to suck a prick which has not been washed. If you don't believe me, consult any etiquette guide…

- Most women are NOT called Linda Lovelace, and do not relish the idea of having about half a foot of penis rammed right down their throats! If you really want to know, Ms Lovelace – the star of *Deep Throat* – achieved her prodigious feats by using a sword-swallower's trick of straightening out her neck so as to make penetration easier. Furthermore, I believe that – like some gay men – she had trained herself to abolish the gag reflex which makes most people feel sick when something touches the back of their throats.

   But the average woman DOES have a gag reflex, and therefore her partner should take care not to thrust more deeply than she's comfortable with. Letting her decide how deep any thrusting should be is a good idea, and helps to allay her understandable fears that she might be choked…

- Finally, a lot of females are unsure or unhappy about coping with male orgasm if it happens during fellatio… We'll deal with *that* particular problem at the end of the chapter.

WHAT POSITION DO YOU DO IT IN?

This is very important! You will find, that a lot of men think that it's an absolutely great idea to do it with you *underneath* – in other words, as if they were having ordinary sexual intercourse with you. To some males, this is inelegantly known as face-fucking. However, most females do NOT find this sort of woman-underneath posture very nice, and it's important that males realize that fact.

With a few exceptions, women do generally like to be *in some sort of control* while they're giving a man head, partly because it's no fun being half-asphyxiated by

SEX PLAY

something which is being forced into you and which you can't push away. (Would YOU like that, guys? No, neither would I…) So in broad terms, it's a good plan to do it in one of the following ways:

- With the man lying flat on his back, so the woman is above him and gradually lowering her face on to his cock.
- With the man sitting on a chair or sofa and the woman sitting or kneeling near him – and bending her head down into his lap.
- With the man standing, and the woman kneeling on the floor in front of him – just as our happy couple are demonstrating in the illustration 113. I believe that a few feminists have occasionally objected to this position, on the grounds that it 'demeans women'. But in fact it is of course exactly like the corresponding cunnilingus position (described in our previous chapter) in which the man happily kneels in down in front of the woman and buries his head gratefully in her pubes.

In practice, many females do almost instinctively adopt this kneeling posture when they go in for fellatio, and use it in order to do all sorts of additional and interesting things to the male with their hands…

- With the couple lying on their sides on the bed, facing toward each other.
- In the famous 69 position – see below (if you'll forgive the pun…).

WHAT DO YOU ACTUALLY DO?

If you ask a lot of inexperienced women what they feel about giving their men oral sex, again and again you find that what puzzles them is the question: *what do you actually do?*

Often, they're afraid of looking foolish, because they're just not sure how mouth-penis contact is supposed to work. One teenage girl wrote to me saying: 'This is really embarrassing in today's world, where everybody is supposed to know everything about sex, and where all one's friends make out that they're expert at giving head to their guys!'

Well, of course people – especially young women – AREN'T generally experts at going down on a partner. But happily, dear readers, it is fairly simple to master the three very basic techniques. These are simply:

- Kissing.
- Licking.
- Sucking.

We'll go into these in much more detail in a minute. Basically though, if you begin by warmly and lovingly kissing your man, you won't go far wrong. As you get more confident, you can progress to giving him nice licks with your tongue – the sort of thing which you'd probably like done to your own sex organs.

Or when you're ready, you can put him in your mouth, if you wish. But don't try any of these things till you've read what I'm about to say on the subject of lubrication during fellatio. The importance of lubrication

These days, most couples have grasped the fact that good lubrication is necessary for sexual intercourse. But it's often forgotten that it's also very necessary for successful oral sex – especially as prolonged firm contact between his penis and your mouth can cause soreness for either one of you. Also, for most couples, 'oiling the wheels' will considerably increase the pleasure and the sense of abandon.

Good *artificial* lubricants – as I've indicated in earlier chapters – include commercial products such as baby oil, sex lotions, contraceptive creams and gels, or even a touch of Vaseline (petroleum jelly). But there are two *caveats*:

- DON'T use an oil-based product (like Vaseline or baby oil) if you're going on to have intercourse with a condom – it will destroy the rubber.
- Obviously, don't pick something that has an unpleasant taste which would put the lady off; some contraceptive creams are definitely a bit yukky in this respect.

What about NATURAL lubricants? If you're squeamish about bodily fluids (as many women and men are), then perhaps you'd better skip this next bit. However, natural secretions are really wonderful for lubricating a man's penis, probably because that's what Nature put them there for. They are:

SEX PLAY

117

- The man's pre-come or pre-ejaculate – which is the small amount of fairly clear fluid which appears at the tip of many men's cocks after you've excited them for a little while. Admittedly, there isn't very much of it, so all you can do is anoint the *head* of his organ with it.
- Your own vaginal secretions, which you can liberally slurp over his shaft – provided that you don't mind the taste of them yourself. (Some women find them a turn-on; others definitely don't).
- Most of all, your saliva. People are very ambivalent about saliva: most highly-sexed couples come to really love it as a sexual lubricant, especially during fellatio. Others can't stand it, and feel sickened by it. The choice is yours. But in fact, the literature about fellatio indicates that many men are delighted if the woman really pours out her mouth-juices on to the head and shaft when she's getting started.

Later in this chapter, we'll deal with the more exotic subject of using food and drink as lubricants.

GETTING STARTED

What do you do when you want to get started? Here's my seven-point plan:

- Make sure that you are comfortable – and (let's be fair) that he is too.
- Make sure that he knows what you're planning to do. Though experienced men will simply *expect* you to give them oral sex at some early stage in your relationship, inexperienced ones probably won't – and may be alarmed at the prospect of female teeth flashing around their pricks!
- Pick some position – as described above – where you (not him) are going to be in reasonable control of what's about to happen.
- Unless you're both very used to fellatio, I suggest that you kick off by just kissing his belly and thighs for a minute or two before you approach his 'naughty bits'.
- Then you can tease him a bit by kissing and nibbling his pubic hair.
- If you're inexperienced, don't let yourself be too rushed by him – even if he tries to grab your head and impale it on his penis.

- When – and *only* when – you're ready, gently start kissing his cock, as described in our next section.

Incidentally, a wacky and highly effective beginning to oral sex on a man who's still got his trousers and/or shorts on is to breathe puffs of air through the front of the garment! Most men are intrigued and excited by the cosy, warm sensation which this produces.

KISSING HIS PENIS

This is a very nice thing to do for him – and, if you're inexperienced or nervous, a very good way to begin. You can get the general idea from the drawing over the page: just apply your pursed lips to his cock, and give him lots of big kisses. It doesn't matter whether he's erect or not at the time; but if you do it while he's non-erect, you'll probably find that this works pretty well as a way of giving him a stiffy. Obviously then, it's a great help to the man who has potency problems.

Move up and down his shaft with your lips, kissing all over the place, and seeing what gives him most pleasure – as well as finding out what you enjoy yourself. You'll get good reactions from him if you concentrate on the following areas (which are shown in the drawing on page 15, back in the anatomy chapter)

- The head of his penis.
- Just below the rim of the head.
- The pleasure ridge.
- The heart area.

Once he's erect, don't hesitate to really concentrate on this heart area – which, as you probably recall, is located on the side of his cock which is furthest from his belly when he's stiff. In particular, press your moist lips against the little string of tissue which runs vertically through the heart area. In an erect male, this usually produces intense and agreeable twitching, plus an increase in the size of his erection.

I well remember that when we were filming my highly explicit Carlton TV series *The Good Sex Guide* we interviewed a beautiful and extremely intelligent young woman who had, in effect, made oral sex on men her hobby in life.

SEX PLAY

kissing his
heart

While I was very concerned about the fact that she had clearly practised on far more partners than is advisable these days, it was most striking that – unlike most women – she had realized the importance of the heart region of the penis at an early age, and had trained herself to stimulate it intensively with her lips.

I need scarcely add that while she was describing her kissing techniques, the male members of the camera crew were rigid with attention. And you can interpret that sentence in any way you like.

SUCKING, TASTE AND THE VACUUM TECHNIQUE

Now let's move swiftly on, from kissing to sucking. Men love this. Putting it bluntly, for many males, having the penis sucked is nothing less than heaven on earth.

But again, if you're inexperienced don't let yourself be rushed. Just take a little of your man's cock in your mouth to begin with – say, the head. Now suck on it firmly; don't worry, you won't hurt him.

Sucking works best if you've got the tip of your tongue just *under* his penis. And don't be afraid to apply plenty of power, so that your cheeks become really hollow.

When you've got used to sucking the head, you can if you wish move on to sucking his entire cock – or at least, as much of it as you feel comfortable with. Do NOT let him force you to take in more than you want. Alternate sucking and relaxing will almost certainly produce a little moisture from his tip – and a beatific smile on his face!

TASTE It's during sucking that you'll probably first notice the taste of your partner's penis. Experienced women tell me that it's an attractive but not particularly strong taste, usually with a tangy or slightly musky flavour it's quite unlike anything else in the world, though I believe that imitations of it have been used in the aftershave industry

Let me stress that it's totally harmless! Provided that your guy washes himself regularly down below, you've nothing to fear at all.

Incidentally, remember that when you kiss his mouth afterwards, he may well be able to taste himself Some fellows may not be able to handle this, though others may find it a turn-on – since the taste shows clearly where your lips have been…

THE VACUUM TECHNIQUE This is a form of sucking which is of tremendous help in treating mild impotence – and indeed in giving succour (sorry!) to any man who finds himself in the very common situation of wanting to summon up an erection.

You can get the picture from the drawing: just take the limp – or even half-erect – penis in your mouth and suck and suck and suck. Use your chest and abdominal muscles to apply all the suction you can to it.

The effect of this is not just to turn your guy on; perhaps more importantly, it draws blood into his cock – and of course it is the inflow of blood to the penis which causes erection. Incidentally once you've got him about half-erect, you can in addition use your hand to stimulate him further and help him on the way to full stiffness.

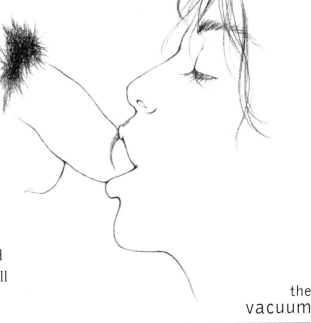

the
vacuum

If more men and women knew about this simple vacuum technique, there would be far less impotence around.

THE LICK OF LOVE

Note: if you've no experience at all of oral sex, you might like to try this BEFORE you attempt sucking your man – especially if you find the idea of licking is less threatening for you.

Tonguing your loved one's penis is a wonderful thing to do for him. He will adore it – and it's quite possible that in the fullness of time, you will come to love it too.

The tongue is, of course, one of the most sensitive parts of the human body, as is shown by the fact that an extraordinarily large area of your brain is devoted to dealing with incoming sensations from this remarkable organ. Also, there's something about its wetness, flexibility, intimacy and sheer sensuality that makes tongue play remarkably exciting for the person who's on the receiving end. (If you enjoy having your clitoris tongued, you'll know what I mean.)

So, lick your man's organ all over – just like the woman in the drawing is doing. You'll find that it works best when he is erect or at least half-erect, but it's also a nice thing to do to him when he's limp.

If you want to get your Ph.D. in phallilingus (a word which I've just made up, solely to use in this book!), then I suggest that you take great care to lick the following areas:

the **lick** of **love**

- His heart zone (of course).
- His pleasure ridge.
- The whole head of his penis
- All the way round the rim of the head.

All these areas are so erotically charged that you might well make him come by licking the – especially if he's young and still rather explosively-triggered. So if he asks you to take it easy (because it's a bit soon for orgasm), I think you should do so.

Less dramatic reactions – but quite interesting ones – can be obtained if you lick:

- His testicles.
- His perineum.
- The sensitive triangle of smooth skin on the underside of his scrotum.

If you're not quite sure where all these tongue-targets are, do go back to Chapter One and have a quick look at the drawings on pages 15 and 18.

THE IN-AND-OUT

The In-and-Out (not to be confused with a gentlemen's club of the same name in London) is one of the commonest and most effective ways of giving head to a man.

All is clear from the drawing overleaf. Position yourself above your partner, and close your lips gradually around the head of his penis. Now begin to move your head forwards and backwards (that is, vertically), so that your lips go down about as far as the places shown in the drawing.

Please note that the more moist your lips are, the better this will go. Lipstick is particularly helpful in aiding you to slide up and down – as are saliva and the other lubricants which I've mentioned earlier.

Vital note (at least, it's a vital note from a bloke's point of view): this caress is the one in which you're particularly likely to catch him with your teeth. Men are TERRIFIED of this – and I can assure you that it's no fun if it happens…

Many female authorities on fellatio say that the best thing to do is to 'cover your teeth with your lips' throughout this technique. But in practice, that isn't awfully easy to do, unless you have large lips and small teeth. So, my advice is just to try to make a conscious effort to keep the tips of your incisors away from your poor old partner's cock. My own experience has been that the two upper front teeth are the most dangerous in this respect; if you're facing your man as you do in the In-and-

SEX PLAY

the
in-and-out

Out, there's a great tendency for your front teeth to scrape painfully down the belly-side of his shaft. He will not be too wild about this...

Make your guy aware that the most important thing for him to remember during the In-an-Out is *not to thrust*. If necessary, break off and tell him that you don't appreciate being choked. There is much to be said for just getting him to lie almost totally still while YOU provide all the movement. As world fellatio authority Ms Tuppy Owens succinctly puts it: 'If you want it, fellas, for heaven's sake keep still so we can get on with it!'

In fact, you can soon learn to limit the distance which his shaft penetrates by simply using your hands to keep him from going in too far. Alas, men do tend to have this slightly barmy idea that they'd like to get as far down your throat as possible – something which is incomprehensible to many females.

But women who are expert in the art of the In-and-Out say that they can often 'fool' a man into thinking that his tip is somewhere deep in the throat by simply using the tongue-tip to direct it *into the inside of the cheek*. Talk about tongue in cheek!

Incidentally, a lot of couples find that during the In-and-Out (and also during other oral techniques), it's quite helpful if the man sometimes gives himself a few strokes with his own hand. This not only affords the woman an occasional much-needed rest, but seems to be useful if the guy has any tendency to lose his erection, or has any difficulty in coming.

THE BUTTERFLY FLICK

The butterfly flick is shown in this drawing. It only works when your man is fully erect – but, boy, does it work!

As you can see what you do is to flick the tip of your tongue across the little string of pink or black tissue which run downwards like a taut bowstring on the heart-side of his penis.

Make little flicking movements from side-to-side and – to be quite frank – you will see his cock literally twitch with delight.

An alternative of the butterfly flick can be practised on the pleasure ridge which you'll remember is slightly lower down on the same side of his penis.

THE SILKEN SWIRL

This famous oral caress was first named by 'J', the anonymous female author of *The Way to Become The Sensuous Woman* – that extraordinary and ground-breaking late Sixties book which was the first to say: 'Yes, it really is OK for a lady to put a guy's cock in her mouth.'

the
butterfly
flick

So naturally, that's what you begin by doing: put your man's stiff (or semi-stiff) penis in your mouth. Now with your lips closed round his shaft, simply swirl your tongue round and round his organ. Try to move your tongue up and down at the same time.

If that sounds complicated, it's not really: all you have to do is to try to trace a spiral around his prick inside your mouth. Keep everything very moist and you won't go far wrong.

COMBINING MOUTH AND HANDS

With most of the oral caresses which I've described so far, it's a good idea to bring your *hands* into play from time to time, as well as your mouth, as shown in the drawing below.

This has several advantages:

- It gives your tired mouth and tongue a rest.
- It gives him added stimulation.
- It helps to maintain his erection.

As I indicated above, there's absolutely no reason why he shouldn't join in with his hands too, provided they aren't otherwise occupied doing something pleasant to you. However, a few old-fashioned men do understandably feel a bit diffident about doing this, and may even (erroneously) believe that there's something wrong with a chap lending a helping hand during a session of oral sex play

the
hand and
mouth together

WHIPPED CREAM AND OTHER DELICACIES

Now we come to the question of using food and drink during fellatio. For some reason, this combination always seems to upset self appointed moralists, probably because the idea of having TWO pleasures at the same time strikes them as thoroughly reprehensible!

Indeed, I remember that when I first suggested in a woman's magazine that it's quite a good idea to lick cream off your partner's penis (maybe with a little cherry on the top), my postbag nearly caught fire with angry letters from outraged male readers. Some bloke actually reported me to the General Medical Council, claiming that I had committed Serious Professional Misconduct by writing something which was (and I quote) 'unsuitable for a female readership'.

Naturally, there were no complaints from women…

Being serious for a moment, in human beings the line between enjoyment of food and feeling nauseated is a very fine one. I can quite see that mixing up food with sexual secretions can make some people feel a bit queasy. So if that applies to you, you'd probably do best to skip this section.

Now… how can you combine food and drink with fellatio in order to give you and your partner a spot of good fun? May I suggest the following:

whipped
cream

- This is an excellent idea for beginners. The woman drinks a cup of tea or coffee, and as soon as she's finished she leans forward and puts her man's penis in her mouth. Out of the corner of your eye, watch a happy grin light up his face as he senses this curiously reassuring warmth…
- In the same way as you can use wine for cunnilingus (as I described in the previous chapter), you can use it in fellatio. If you, are a keen oenophile (i.e. wine-bibber) then there's a lot to be said for pouring half a glass of something like that excellent Sicilian stuff called *Corvo Bianco* over his erect organ, and then lapping it up. This is an offer that he is most unlikely to refuse…

- You can indeed use whipped cream – like the lady in the drawing on the previous page – thereby fulfilling one of the ultimate male fantasies! However, whipped cream is actually packed full of both calories and cholesterol, so if you're going to do this sort of thing on a regular basis, it might be wiser to substitute something a bit healthier, such as yoghurt.

- Other creamy foods are always popular with couples who are into fellatio. They include: ice cream, chocolate sauce and even – in certain circles – custard. Don't make things too cold or too hot, or you'll end up blowing something more than his mind.

- Fromage frais. I must confess that I'd never have thought of using this till we interviewed the above-mentioned brilliant and beautiful young woman for the TV series *The Good Sex Guide*. This gifted and articulate fellatrix (the correct term for a lady who does fellatio) waxed quite lyrical about the delicious effects she could create with that well-known French low-calorie dessert.

- Honey, jam, jelly and so on. Men usually love it if you lick this kind of thing off them. Assuming you like these tastes yourself, then give them a whirl when you're in the mood. Obviously, with sticky/stainy things, it's essential to have lots of tissues or wipes beside the bed.

- Alternating hot and cold. I am indebted for this suggestion to Ms Kimberley Lesson, who has made a special study of fellatio for *Bite* magazine. She recommends filling your mouth with something moderately hot, then sucking your man – and then filling your mouth with something cold and doing it again, continuing to alternate for as long as you like. She specifies:

HOT THINGS: tea; coffee; cocoa; hot toddy (whisky and water).
COLD THINGS: Stolichnaya vodka and cranberry; Champagne; Diet Pepsi.

Given the choice between Diet Pepsi and decent champagne, I just don't know what to say. Life presents such difficult decisions, doesn't it?

THE JEWEL IN THE MOUTH

Leaving techniques which you use on your man's penis, we move on to what you can do to his testicles, and adjacent zones.

The main thing I have to say to you here, *is be careful.* Us chaps are EXTREMELY sensitive about our balls, and absolutely terrified of anyone doing anything that might injure them. So teeth and testicles are not generally a good mix.

However, it's perfectly in order to kiss and lick your man's scrotum – particularly the highly sensitive underside. And if you're both really adventurous, you can try The Jewel in the Mouth.

What you do is shown in the drawing. Having told your partner what you're planning (most important!), you just open your mouth wide and gently take one of his testicles into it. Don't do anything else; just lie there. My experience is that this technique is a heck of a turn-on for many women, who relish the warmth and intimacy of holding the man's sex gland in their mouths. But for most blokes (except those exotic souls who like being dominated) The Jewel in the Mouth is an experience of slightly limited sensual value. Still, it may be worth trying.

the
jewel in
the mouth

Incidentally, if you happen to have had quite a lot of dental work done in the past, you could call this posture The Jewel in the Crowns…

THE 69

I've already briefly mentioned the famous 69 caress in the previous chapter, which is all about cunnilingus. But now let's look at it from a woman's point of view – and specifically from the point of view of a woman who's trying to give her man fellatio during the course of a quick bout of 69-ing.

Look first at the illustration on the next page, which shows a couple enthusiastically going in for the famous *soixante-neuf.* As you can see, their bodies make a shape which is VERY roughly similar to the two figures '6' and '9'.

SEX PLAY

the 69

Now if you're in this woman's position, I hope that you'll enjoy being given cunnilingus by your guy But up at your end (so to speak), here you are faced with his penis. What do you do?

Well, to some extent it depends on your relative heights. This subject is rarely discussed, but it is a fact that a big difference in height can make the 69 almost impossible. If you're pretty TALL and he is fairly SHORT, you'll probably find that your face is about half-way down his thighs. I feel that your best move here is to try to bend your head well forward so that you can at least kiss and lick his balls and the lower part of his erect penis.

On the other hand, if you are SHORT and he is TALL, you may well find that your face finishes up at about the level of his navel. In this case, your best move is probably to stick your tongue out as far as possible in the hope of reaching the tip of his cock…

But for an *averaged-sized* couple, the odds are that things will fit together reasonably well in the 69 position. However, I have to admit that it's not as easy as some sex manuals (and, of course, the ruder romantic novels) make out. In particular, some women feel quite threatened and uncomfortable when men try to get them into the 69.

My own view is that you, as a women, need to insist on being in a position that you feel totally comfortable with. Bear in mind that there are three ways of doing the famous *soixante-neuf*:

- With you flat on your back and your man on top of you – but a lot of females don't like this much and feel crushed by the guy's weight.
- With HIM on his back and you on top – quite a few women feel that they have better control in this situation.
- With the two of you *on your sides* on the bed – this seems to work quite well for most couples.

I'd ask you to remember that the 69 presents a slight problem for your male partner: breathing! Women (apart, of course, from lesbians) are generally unaware of the fact that it's quite difficult for a lover to draw breath when the mouth and nose are buried between your thighs.

So it really is a good idea to keep your legs a little bit apart if possible, so as to give the poor bloke some room. If you're one of the small number of women who can't come with your thighs spread wide apart, then it's probably best to regard the 69 as a spot of fun along the way to an orgasm – rather than as a position for climaxing in.

Incidentally, *simultaneous* climaxing during the *soixante-neuf* is achievable, but can be quite difficult. This is mainly because of the near-total lack of communication which the position involves. It's almost impossible for you and your man to give each other any helpful hints as to how things are going – unless, of course, you ring each other up on your mobile phones.

Anyway, assuming that you've both settled down comfortably on the bed, and he's giving you a nice tonguing down below, and you've managed to get your head close to his penis, what do you do?

Basically, you just go in for sucking and kissing and licking – though most men will prefer you to concentrate on the sucking. You should also use your two hands to stimulate him. In fact, having your hands in on the action is a good idea from your own point of view too – because they enable you to control things and to prevent him from going in for the shove-it-down-her-throat thrusting which so many women dread when somebody suggests a 69.

The other thing that so many females worry about is this: what on earth do you do if he comes? And that's what we're going to deal with in a moment.

SHOULD YOU MAKE HIM COME?

If you give a chap *any* kind of oral sex – and I don't just mean in the 69 position – you have to think about the possibility of bringing him to orgasm, either deliberately or accidentally

Yes, accidents do happen: the stimulation of a woman's mouth is so powerful that it's sometimes quite difficult for the man to stop himself from coming, especially if he's young and ejaculates very easily. So at times it's wise to take it a little bit easy

Remember, you don't HAVE to try to make him climax; fellatio needn't necessarily lead to male orgasm. Many couples will indulge in a spot of cocksucking for, say, five or ten minutes, and then move on to finishing off in some other way

– having intercourse, for instance. But a lot of men do think that once you offer oral sex, you're going to take them all the way…

So I would recommend that you try to sort out *beforehand* whether you're going to fellate him to orgasm or not: this avoids misunderstandings, which can actually be quite upsetting for some couples. Bear in mind, that once you've sucked or licked your man to climax, that's probably the end of his sexual action for the night – or at least for a while. He may be able to satisfy you with various forms of sex play after he's climaxed (that is, if he deigns to stay awake), but unless he's a most unusually virile male there will be no prospect of intercourse for an hour or so – and, in some cases, for perhaps very much longer.

MALE AND FEMALE ATTITUDES TO COMING DURING FELLATIO

It's important to realize that men and women tend to have very different attitudes to the question of coming during fellatio. The 'Sex in the 1990s' survey carried out jointly by a men's magazine and a women's magazine (*Arena* and *New Woman* respectively) revealed an extraordinary gulf between the sexes. For instance, many female readers were stunned by the revelation that 55 per cent of men wanted to climax in women's mouths – and then see them swallow the ejaculate. '*Most peculiar!*' said one woman editor when she realized that this meant that the majority of males regarded her tonsils as a legitimate (nay, highly desirable) target for their sperms.

I think it would perhaps help readers to avoid misunderstandings with their partners if I tried to sum up the viewpoints of the two sexes.

MALE VIEWS If we leave aside guys who are gay and guys who are not very interested in sex, we're left with somewhere around 70 per cent of men (depending on whose survey you believe) who are keen on being given fellatio by females.

I'm afraid, Madam, that the great majority of these do want to come in your mouth. And as that *New Woman/Arena* survey showed, most of these men would like you to swallow it.

From a male point of view then, fellatio is usually perceived as being very similar to vaginal intercourse: to be blunt, the general idea for many guys is that you put your penis inside a woman's moist and welcoming orifice – and then you pump spunk into it, getting it as deep inside as possible. If you asked them to think about it, they'd probably say that that's the way Nature intended it… ('It's natural, isn't it?')

FEMALE VIEWS It's very important for men to realize that most females simply do not see fellatio as a way of having sperm pumped inside them! Though women vary a great deal in their attitudes to giving head, few of them view it in a very orgasm-orientated sort of fashion.

They're much more likely to perceive fellatio as a warm, intimate thing they can do for their men – a tender, loving gesture, rather than something which is simply intended to produce a volcano of sperm. So an unsuspecting or sexually-inexperienced lady is quite likely to be shocked and stunned by some chap suddenly deciding to shoot his load down the back of her throat. *Guys: do not underestimate the distress and ill-feeling this might cause.*

I have found that women fall into FIVE main groups where this question of male climax during fellatio is concerned:

THE ANTI-FELLATIONIST GROUP Men readers should grasp that there's a substantial minority of women, mainly of feminist persuasion, who have very hostile feelings about fellatio and about male orgasm in the mouth or near the face – because they regard it all as just one more manifestation of male control over females. The above-mentioned survey quoted a respondent called Joanne (age 37) as saying: 'The mere thought of having a penis in my mouth turns my stomach. Apart from the taste and discomfort, I think it's terribly degrading for women. Fellatio is the ultimate power trip for a man.'

I ask male readers to appreciate that these views are intense and sincerely held; you disregard them at your peril.

THE 'IT'S YUKKY' GROUP This is a body of women who have grown up regarding seminal fluid as rather sticky, messy stuff, about as appealing as half-fried egg-white for breakfast. Even during sexual intercourse, they tend not to be very keen on it, and would much prefer that it was enclosed within a nice, tidy condom…

SEX PLAY

135

They tend to talk about spunk as being 'slimy' – and I must say, I have a certain sympathy with them; I'm quite grateful that I'm a bloke and don't have to have it in my mouth! However, some women who are experienced at blow jobs do tell me that in fact it's *not* slimy-tasting at all.

THE SILENT MAJORITY And why are they silent? Because their mouths are full, of course. (Sorry: this old joke goes back as far as Oscar Wilde, I believe.) Seriously, a very large group of women love their men and are willing to put up with what they regard as the slightly daft male notion that it's a good idea to splash one's come around one's partner's mouth.

These females don't find it a colossal turn-on, but they don't mind doing it to oblige – which is very decent of them.

THE 'IT'S YUMMY' GROUP In contrast, there's a minority of women who are really very excited by giving oral sex to a man. They feel that fellatio is a delightful service to offer someone they love – and if you come, they regard it as a tribute to their oral skills and their femininity.

And, incredible as it may seem to their more restrained sisters, they seem to love a partner's seminal fluid, and will happily rub it into their breasts and clitorises after he comes. That extraordinary fellatrix who we interviewed for The Good Sex Guide TV series said that she adored feeling it flow into her mouth – following which she took great pleasure in dribbling it back over her partner's organ.

In short, women like this seem to have a tremendous empathy for male sexual secretions much the same way that most males feel about female secretions, really.

But such women are, alas, few and far between! No, dear gentlemen readers, I cannot put you in touch with any of these agreeable females.

THE PRACTICAL GROUP Another group – mostly composed of younger females such as students and businesswomen – seems to have emerged in the early 21st century. In their circles, it's often considered preferable to suck a man into a climax rather than allow him to have vaginal intercourse with you.

According to reports, the pragmatic view of these young women is that making sure a male comes off orally tends to avoid any problems with attempted date-rape which might otherwise arise later that night. (If that's true, this is a pretty terrible indictment of male sexuality.)

It appears that the practically-minded students in this group feel that cocksucking a man keeps the woman in control – and also avoids any risk of pregnancy. But for health risks, please see the end of this chapter.

WHAT TO DO AT THE MOMENT OF CLIMAX

If you do let him come while you're giving him fellatio, how on earth do you cope with the liquid?

The etiquette of this problem has been extensively explored by women's magazines – with their customary and praiseworthy candour – in the last few years, and it's clear that women have various ways of dealing with a partner's ejaculate. They are:

- You can insist he wears a condom, which will act as a 'catcher' for his fluid. Drawbacks: you get a bit of a rubbery taste; he may complain bitterly; the sheath may snag on your teeth and break. Good point: less risk of HIV or hepatitis transmission.
- You can agree to take it in your mouth, but afterwards discreetly spit it out into some clean tissues. He may feel a bit rejected by this, but that's tough. (However, try not to look disgusted, as some women do…).
- An answer which is popular with men: at the last second, you can direct it on to your breasts. Males, simple souls that we are, usually delight in seeing their own ejaculate shooting across a roguish pair of nipples.
- I say this with considerable trepidation, but some women do deflect the penis at the last moment so that the partner's 'cum' goes on to their faces. I remember once explaining this common practice to a friend of mine who was a lesbian and a strong feminist: she was absolutely appalled!

  But it is a fact that there are a lot of males who are terrifically turned on by this experience. That is why so many of the adult films which are transmitted in hotel chains in Europe and America show the man reaching a climax in precisely this way (this is known as a 'money

SEX PLAY

shot'). However, I must confess that I am a little worried about the implications of all this: it's easy to see a situation where a man could use a 'splash in the face' to make a woman feel degraded and cheap.

- Finally, you can if you wish *swallow* it – of which more in a moment.

IS THE TASTE OF HIS EJACULATE A PROBLEM?

Many women – like Joanne, mentioned above – are disgusted by the idea of tasting seminal fluid. But is it a real problem? Rather surprisingly, females who taste it a lot say 'No'. Semen has a slightly salty and slightly bitter taste. But depending on which part of your tongue it lands on, you may taste nothing at all. Physiologists say that the tip and sides of the tongue detect salty tastes, while the back of the tongue detects bitter ones. Certainly, women who swallow sperm say that it's at the moment of gulping it down that they feel a brief, bitterish tang at the very back of the mouth. From my researches, I have compiled the following observations by women about the question of flavour:

- Some of them report that different men have different-tasting fluid.
- Some say that the taste is stronger if a man hasn't had sex for a long time.
- Several of them claim that the flavour is somehow connected with what the man has been eating recently. I have no idea whether that's true, but I have heard of one woman who disliked the usual flavour of her husband's liquid – so she fed him cinnamon toast beforehand.
- Most women who regularly go in for fellatio say that they're actually happy with the taste.
- The small 'dew drop' which most men produce well before they come is apparently tasteless (just like a lot of this chapter, really…).

THE VEXED QUESTION OF SWALLOWING

Finally, we arrive at that big question: do you swallow it if he comes?

My suggestion is this: *only if you really want to.* Don't let yourself get pressured into it! Men are awfully good at saying reproachful things like 'If you really cared for me, darling, you'd swallow it down like that girl in *Deep Throat*. It's not much to ask, is it?'

Well, it IS quite a lot to ask, actually And remember: it's your throat and your stomach – so it's up to you to decide what you swallow.

One response you could make to male pressure is to ask him what would happen if the roles were reversed. In other words, would he cheerfully swallow your juices – particularly if you were one of the small minority of women who ejaculate at the moment of climax? But I must warn you that you have to be prepared for the fact that many men would answer 'Yes'!

If you're NOT interested in swallowing your lover's semen, then skip the rest of this section. But if you think you might, then let me conclude with a few bits of advice:

- The VOLUME is much less than most women (and most men) imagine. If you look at the teat on the end of a condom, which holds the ejaculated semen, you'll see how very small it is. On average, a chap ejaculates about a teaspoonful, which is 5 cc. It may occasionally go up to 10 cc, especially if your partner hasn't had sex for some days. *Department of Useless Information*: it's because of the volume of male ejaculate that the two world-famous rock bands 10 c.c. and The Lovin' Spoonful got their names. Honestly. It's a Trivial Pursuit question, so it must be true.

- Swallowing it cannot get you pregnant, except under truly bizarre circumstances. The only case which I know of in medical literature occurred in South Africa: a young woman gave her new lover oral sex and swallowed his semen. Her previous lover then burst in through the door and, in a fit of jealous rage, stabbed her in the stomach. She was rushed to hospital, where immediate surgery fortunately saved her life. Several weeks later, it was discovered that she was pregnant. As she had a congenital abnormality of her gynaecological organs which made it impossible for her to be fertilized by vaginal intercourse, the doctors concluded that – as a result of the knife wound to her stomach – the swallowed sperms had managed to make their way through her belly to her ovary.

 I think you can probably say that all this is a trifle unlikely to happen to you. I hope.

- There are a very few women who are mad keen on swallowing semen, and who claim that it is good for their skin. As a doctor, I find this very hard to believe.

- Dame Nellie Melba, the great Australian soprano, is said to have made a habit of doing it just before she went on stage 'to lubricate her throat'. God knows what Caruso thought of this.

- Contrary to anything you may have heard, a man's juices are NOT fattening. They contain virtually no calories. As I write, I am looking at an American cartoon in which a young woman is saying to her bed-partner: 'The other things I like about it are that it's low-fat, low-sodium, caffeine-free, and contains no sugar or preservatives.'
  I'm very doubtful about the low-sodium; but the rest is right…

- Finally, if the love of your life happens to be a keen literary man, bear in mind that his whole attitude to swallowing will probably have been influenced by Molly Bloom's famous soliloquy in James Joyce's *Ulysses*, in which the lady says (and I don't apologize for her lack of punctuation):

'I often felt I wanted to kiss him all over also his lovely young cock there so simply I wouldn't mind taking him in my mouth if nobody was looking as if it was asking you to suck it so clean and white he looked with his boyish face I would too in $^1/_2$ a minute even if some of it went down what its only like gruel or the dew.'

Did she have half a pint of Guinness afterwards, I wonder? Very probably.

HEALTH WARNING

Ordinarily, fellatio is a very safe activity. But please bear the following points in mind:

- Do NOT do it for a man if he has any kind of sore or raw place on his penis.
- Do not do it if he has any kind of discharge.
- Do not do it if you yourself have a nose, throat or mouth infection.
- Especially, don't do it if you have a cold sore (*herpes simplex*) on your

mouth. If you don't know what a cold sore is, it's that very common blistery eruption which comes out on many people's upper or lower lips from time to time. In some countries, it's known as a 'fever blister' or a 'canker sore'. And it's very infectious.

It's usually acquired in childhood, and is caused by a variety of the herpes virus. During an eruption, you shouldn't even be kissing anybody, let alone giving them oral sex!

- If your partner asks you to BLOW during fellatio, *refuse*. You could fill his plumbing up with germs.

HIV What about HIV risks? While strictly monogamous couples have nothing much to fear, those who stray from the straight and narrow obviously expose themselves to a certain degree of risk. Incidence of heterosexual HIV is on the increase again. And if neither of you has HIV, then clearly you can forget all about any risk from fellatio. However, where there is the slightest possibility that either partner has the virus, you must of course take care. Although at the moment, the AIDS charities are saying that the risk of getting HIV from fellatio is relatively low, the danger would be greater:

- If he comes in your mouth.
- If you have any cuts or raw places in your mouth. For this reason, there are some couples who always do it with a condom, just in case.

GENERAL HEALTH Finally, I'd ask women readers of this chapter to note the fact that if you observe anything unusual when you're going down on your partner (such as lumps in the testicle or groin, or raw patches on the penis), please tell him – and get him to have these lesions checked out by his doc. In particular, testicular tumours are very common in younger men, and do occur in older ones; so look out for lumps.

SEX PLAY

vibrator techniques for a man to use on a woman

WHY USE A VIBRATOR?

Though women in the Orient have used vibrating devices as 'self-pleasurers' for a very long time, they were almost unknown in the West till the end of the Swinging Sixties. In 1969, Dr David Reuben published his best seller *Everything You Always Wanted To Know About Sex (but were afraid to ask)*, in which he revealed to an astonished world that large numbers of American women were buying 'heavy-duty muscle massagers' – and using them to stimulate their clitorises.

Could it be true? Well, of course it was. Soon afterwards, I pointed out in my column in a British women's magazine that the beauty aid massagers being widely sold in UK chemists' shops and electrical goods stores would make excellent sex play toys. A few months later, the PR-person for one of the large manufacturers of these beauty massagers discreetly thanked me for the sudden rise in sales…
(And I haven't had the cheque yet, madam.)

Since those days, literally tens of millions of vibrators *specially shaped for sex*, and unashamedly advertised as sex aids, have been sold throughout the Western world. Why? What's the point of them?

Well, as Top Agony Aunt Suzie Hayman says in her book *Good Vibrations*: 'Vibrators give sexual pleasure by trembling rhythmically.' The 'trembling' is caused by a little electric motor, which spins a head round and round inside the device.

And the main reasons for the success of vibrators are as follows:

- They provide an extraordinarily convenient way of stimulating women's sexy bits (and, to a lesser extent, men's sexy bits) with practically no effort.

using a
vibrator on her

- They vibrate very, very fast indeed – faster than the human hand or tongue could manage.
- They're very useful (and please don't laugh at this) for the large number of people with arthritis or other disabilities of the hand which make regular sex play difficult.
- The intensity of their stimulus helps many women to reach orgasm – which is why they're now widely used by sex therapists to treat non-orgasmic patients.
- That intense stimulus also helps some men with erection difficulties.
- They are FUN!

Now I'm not suggesting that vibrators are everybody's cup of tea. But for many couples (like the pair in our illustration on page 145) who've been together for a while and want to bring an occasional touch of extra spice into their love-making, they're absolutely fine.

Clearly, there are times when a vibe would be totally inappropriate in a relationship. For instance, a romantic young man who's deeply in love with a beautiful girl wouldn't dream of producing a vibrator when he takes her out on a date – any more than Romeo would have packed one in his tights when he climbed up to Juliet's balcony

But, if Juliet had lived to 41 instead of 14, then it might have been a different matter…

DO MANY MEN AND WOMEN USE THEM?

Yes – surprising as it may be to people who've never thought about a vibrator (and maybe wouldn't be seen dead with one), they do.

As I've said above, vibrators sell in their tens of millions these days. There are whole factories in the Far East which are dedicated to turning them out for sale to the West. It's because so many are produced that the prices of vibrators are almost laughably low: you can get a perfectly satisfactory one for the price of a round of drinks.

In one of my recent surveys, conducted among 6000 pretty sophisticated British women, it emerged that 40 per cent had used vibrators – and most of them liked the experience. Usage was much more common in the more mature age groups.

Some of these women were using the devices for self-pleasuring, but many more kept them for use in the kind of sex play techniques that we'll describe in a moment.

THE VARIOUS TYPES OF VIBRATOR

You can still get vibrators like the beauty aids and muscle massagers that I mentioned earlier. They tend to be shaped rather like pistols, with a vibrating latex head where the muzzle of the gun would be. When you switch them on, this head starts shaking about, to the accompaniment of a buzzing noise – one of the few drawbacks of vibrators is the fact that they usually make a devil of a racket! (Not a good feature if you live in a place with thin walls…)

These rather old-fashioned pistol-style vibrators are mostly mains-powered, so you need a convenient power-point for them. I know of one highly-sexed woman journalist who unashamedly keeps two of them permanently plugged in at her bedside. Just in case, you understand.

For heavens' sake, do not use mains-powered vibrators near water or in the bath. Battery-powered vibrators, which I'm just about to come to, can be used near water without fear of electrocution, but unless they're marked 'waterproof', don't take them into the bath or shower or they'll stop working.

In fact, the vast majority of vibrators sold these days are powered by small batteries. Regrettably, most of them are penis-shaped – doubtless designed by a man who thought that was what women would want. (However, lesbian sex play textbooks describe them as 'vagina-shaped'.) If you're a chap, don't fall into the common trap of ramming one of these phallic-shaped devices up your partner and thinking that's all you need do. There are far more sensitive ways of using a vibrator (even a penis-like one), as we'll see in a moment.

It is also possible to buy vibrators which have other shapes, for instance the world famous 'Non Doctor' which is cylindrical and has a series of different heads – flat, bumpy, cupped and so on – from which the woman can choose.

Worldwide, the majority of vibrators are still made of hard plastic. But Scandinavian sex shops have introduced a range of much softer, latex-covered (and often pliable) vibrators. You can now buy these in most countries. The new 'jelly-feel' vibrators are also very popular, probably because they have a much warmer, nicer feel than a plastic 'vibe'.

USING A VIBRATOR ON YOUR PARTNER'S CLITORIS

RULE ONE Tell her what you propose to do, especially if she's had no previous experience of vibrators.

RULE TWO Make sure she's agreeable!

RULE THREE Ensure that the vibrator is WARM – a cold chunk of plastic on the clitoris is not very romantic.

RULE FOUR Consider LUBRICATING the tip of the vibrator, so that it'll slip easily over her delicate tissues.

RULE FIVE Don't even THINK about switching it on till you've thoroughly romanced and cuddled her, and made her feel wanted.

RULE SIX If she's at all doubtful, give her the vibrator and let her work round her clitoris with it herself.

'Working round' is basically what you do, as shown in the drawing below. Just as

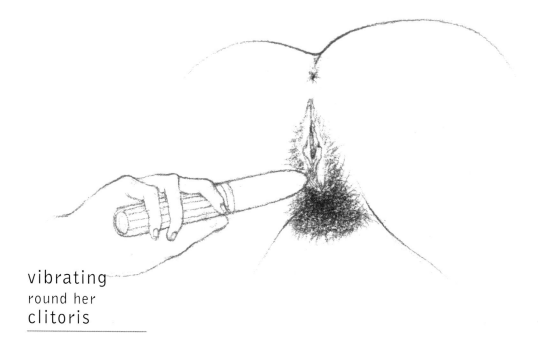

vibrating
round her
clitoris

you would with finger and tongue caresses, *keep moving*. Don't hang about on one spot for long – unless she specifically asks you to. Again, unless she specifically demands it, don't start on her clitoris itself. Begin at least 1 inch (2.5 cm) away, and work towards the little organ over a period of several minutes. Be very gradual and gentle about approaching the sensitive tip.

Above all, be guided by her. If she wants to have an orgasm with the device on or near her clitoris, then let her. And good luck to her!

USING A VIBRATOR IN HER VAGINA

Although I've said above that you shouldn't ram a vibrator crudely up your partner's vagina, there's no doubt that when the mood is right many women do enjoy having one placed slowly and sensuously inside the cunny.

The phrase 'when the mood is right' implies that you shouldn't try it until your partner is thoroughly warmed up – and enthusiastic about what you're going to do.

You MUST lubricate the tip and shaft of the vibrator, using either her love juices

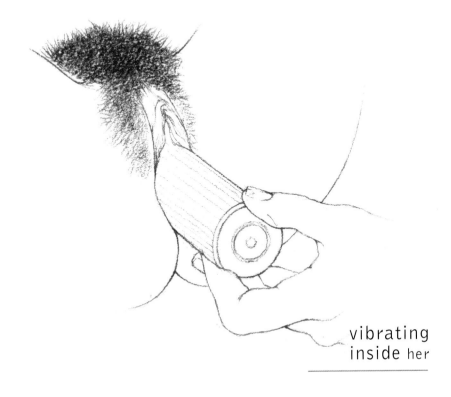

vibrating
inside her

or some artificial help. Then, like the man in the drawing here, very carefully insert the tip between her inner lips and gently push it in. Only go in as far as she wants you to.

You can switch it on before you put it in or afterwards – experiment with both methods, and see which she prefers. And when you've got it in, do use the vibrating part of the shaft to lovingly push her inner lips apart and so stretch the S-zone (see Chapter Two).

Finally, using the vibrator inside her cunt offers you the ideal opportunity to give her *simultaneous* clitoral stimulation with your fingertips or your mouth (if it's the latter, just ignore that buzzing in your ears.) You probably remember that many females need this double stimulation – stretching the vagina combined with friction on the clitoris – if they are to reach orgasm easily

TRYING FOR HER G-SPOT WITH A VIBRATOR

I explained all about the Famous Female G-spot in Chapter Two. Inevitably, people have come up with a G-spot vibrator; this has a bend in the head, so that the man can direct the tip up towards the woman's Graefenberg spot (to give the G-spot its correct name), as shown in the drawing below.

Frankly, I have to say that unless you're a gynaecologist you will not find it easy to get the head of the vibrator on to her G-spot region. Even if you're successful

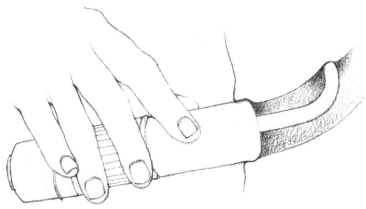

the
g-spot vibrator

immediately, it's possible that the vibrator won't give her sensations as good as those she would get from the finger caresses of the spot described in Chapter Three.

Nonetheless, it's worth a try – especially if both of you have fun searching. *Bonne chance!*

THE ANGEL'S EGG

The Angel's Egg (sometimes known as Angel's Delight) is – not surprisingly – a little egg-shaped vibrator, connected to a small battery pack by a wire.

The vibrating part is about half the size of a hen's egg, and the general idea is that you pop it just inside your partner's opening, thus dilating her S-zone. Then you switch it on, and it sort of sits there and throbs

Very nice – and quite a useful aid to orgasm, especially if at the same time you use your lips or fingers sensitively on her clitoris.

THE BUTTERFLY VIBRATOR

Entirely different is the butterfly vibrator – often known as Joni's butterfly. I've never been able to find out who Joni was, I'm afraid.

The butterfly, which is sometimes actually shaped just like a *papillon's* wings – is a vibrating device which you just strap in front of your loved one's vulva, using those four little straps which go round behind her bottom. Then you switch it on, and it starts jigging about.

On the inner side are a lot of little latex bumpy bits, and the general plan is that these rub up and down against your partner's clitoris and her vulva generally. I hope she likes this. Presumably Joni did, though she's been very quiet recently… Some versions of Joni's butterfly have bumps on the *outside*, so that if you wish you can lie against your partner and enjoy a little vibratory stimulation too.

In 2001, a new Japanese version of the butterfly (sold under the trade-name 'Micro Butterfly') was introduced. This is a smaller, jelly-soft vibrator, held on by an adjustable thong. The butterfly is so small that it can actually be worn over the clitoris during sex.

Another new variant is the 'Oriental Dragonfly', which incorporates a vaginal probe and a tail which curves around to the anus.

SEX PLAY

HYGIENE NOTE

Finally, just a few points about vibrator hygiene:

- Never put a vibrator anywhere near your partner unless it is scrupulously clean.

- After use, give it a very thorough wiping with a facecloth or sponge which has been dipped in warm, soapy water. Then dry it carefully with a clean towel or tissues, or allow it to dry in the air.

- Under no circumstances should the same vibrator be used on two different women. This could spread infection.

- If, like many couples, you sometimes use the vibrator on the lady's bottom in the way mentioned in Chapter Eleven, then remember that under no circumstances must it touch her vulva after it has touched her anus.

- There is a type of vibrator – quite common in the USA but not elsewhere – which has twin probes that vibrate both the woman's vagina AND her rectum. If you decide to try this, you must make sure that the rectal probe never goes anywhere near her vagina.

And now on to our next chapter, which is about how a woman can use a vibrator on her man. I hope it'll give you a buzz…

8

VIBRATOR TECHNIQUES FOR A WOMAN TO USE ON A MAN

NOT JUST A TOY FOR WOMEN

There's no doubt that the overwhelming majority of vibrators are used by women – or rather, in most cases, ON women by men.

But the rapid buzzing of a vibrator can also be a stimulus to the sexually arousable parts of the average male. So, if you occasionally fancy applying your personal vibe to the erotic bits of your loved one, you'll probably find that he enjoys it.

There are a few vibrators made specifically for men, and we'll describe those in a moment. But most couples who use these toys simply share a vibrator with each other. For instance, after the man has applied the device to the woman's clitoris for a few minutes, she may take it from him and put it on his penis.

In other words, pretty well all vibrators can be regarded as unisex.

AN AID TO ERECTION

In recent years, it's become clear that a vibrator can sometimes be quite a help when the penis is tired and doesn't want to get itself erect.

For that reason, quite a few sex clinics now recommend vibrators as part of the therapy in cases of impotence. Please note that I only say part of the therapy – impotence may require very much more complicated treatment than just slapping a vibrator on the man's cock.

Nonetheless, if your partner is sometimes a little slow to get a stiffy, then you could do worse than buy him one of these devices, and lovingly apply it to his penis, testicles and perineum.

Incidentally, you can buy a vibe without embarrassment in most Western countries these days. If you don't want to go to a sex shop, you simply buy it by mail. Order without embarrassment from PASSION 8 (tel. 0870 90 888 99, or www. Passsion8shop.com).

In Britain, there are now several sex shops catering exclusively for women (men must be accompanied by a female). It's the easiest thing in the world for women to go in and buy a vibrator. The best-known such shop is SH! (Women's Erotic Emporium) at 43 Coronet Street, London N1 6HD tel. 0207-613 5458.

APPLYING A VIBRATOR TO THE HEART OF THE PENIS

A good way to use your vibrator on your man is to apply it to the heart – the very sensitive area just below the head – as shown in the drawing below. A device with a flat end, like the one shown, seems to work best here.

For good results in the heart area, apply the vibrator when your partner is already partially or fully erect.

APPLYING A VIBRATOR TO THE SHAFT

If you want to arouse a limp penis, it's usually best to apply the vibrator to your man's shaft. This will – with luck – encourage blood to flow into the three big cylinders which lie inside his cock, so creating an erection.

You can also apply the vibrator to his shaft when he's fully erect, as shown in the drawing 156. Working up and down the pleasure ridge (see page 15 in Chapter One to remind yourself where it is) is usually very effective.

Incidentally, some guys may not be happy with having penile contact with the type of vibrator shown in our drawing – simply because it's penis-shaped. If that's the case with your bloke, then you'd better select a different model. (Of vibrator, that is – not of bloke.)

APPLYING IT UNDERNEATH

If your man has a sense of fun, then he'll appreciate it if you apply your little vibrator to his underparts – in other words:

vibrating
his heart

- To his testicles (take it easy).
- To the smooth triangle of skin hidden underneath his scrotum – as explained in Chapter One, this area is

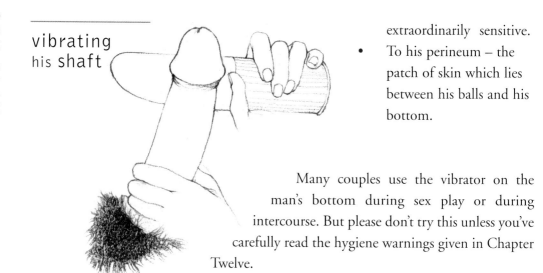

vibrating
his shaft

extraordinarily sensitive.

- To his perineum – the patch of skin which lies between his balls and his bottom.

Many couples use the vibrator on the man's bottom during sex play or during intercourse. But please don't try this unless you've carefully read the hygiene warnings given in Chapter Twelve.

THE PENISATOR

The Penisator – shown in the illustration opposite – is an ingenious invention which you fix on to the base of your man's shaft – and then switch on!

It seems to be quite successful at producing erotic sensation and, perhaps more importantly, it would be useful for a man with minor erection problems.

Perhaps a good birthday present to give your man when he turns eighty?

A similar device is the new 'Dual Fun' set – which vibrates on the penis but also stimulates the clitoris when the genitals are in contact.

OTHER MALE VIBRATORS

There are other male vibrators which you may possibly like to try out on your man. For instance:

THE HANDSTRAP You strap this one to your own hand, and then take his cock in your fingers. When you switch on, the vibration of the device is transmitted through your hand to him. Interesting.

THE SUCKER This curious device is rather like a woman's mouth. You put it over your guy's penis, so that the 'lips' are about half-way down the shaft. Then you switch it on and it sucks him rhythmically

THE ARTIFICIAL VAGINA This is most often used by male, solo masturbators. But it would be of some value to a couple if the woman were *disabled* and couldn't use her own vagina. The vibrator looks like a vulva, but is fitted with an electric trembler inside.

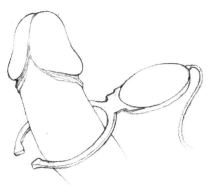

the
penisator

SEX PLAY

using a vibrator
on him

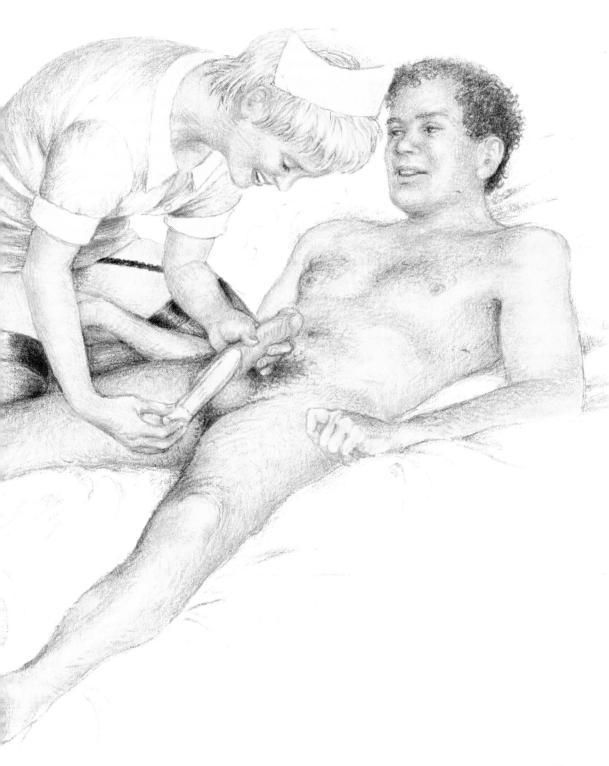

9

OTHER SEX AID TECHNIQUES FOR A MAN TO USE ON A WOMAN

HUNDREDS OF AIDS FOR SEX PLAY

Apart from vibrators, there are literally hundreds of different types of sex aid on the market.

But my surveys of couples' bedtime behaviour indicate that very few Western women have ever been on the receiving end of anything other than a vibrating device. This does rather suggest that most of these other aids aren't very successful.

Still, there are a very few of them which can be fun for an adventurous couple to try out. And, more significantly perhaps, there are one or two which are genuinely helpful to handicapped people.

In this chapter, we'll look at the sex aids which the man can use in order to pleasure the woman - and in the next chapter, it'll be *vice versa*.

Most of the aids which I'm going to describe in these two chapters can be bought very cheaply from sex shops or by mail order. But one or two are things which you probably have in your home already: it only requires a little ingenuity to turn them into sex aids…

NIPPLE STIMULATORS

The new nipple stimulators are greatly amusing. They include:

- The Nipple Super Sucker – draws the nipple out and stimulates it.
- The Universal Nipple Enlarger – uses small pumps and rings to tease and enlarge the nipple.
- The Crystal Clamps – adjustable transparent clamps – a non-traumatic alternative to nipple-piercing!

BOOBY DROPS

Although this chapter is supposed to be about pleasuring women, I'm not sure who is meant to get most pleasure from this particular aid.

Booby drops, as you can see from our illustration, are liquids which come in little bottles – and which you're supposed to put on your partner's nipples. You then suck them off (if you'll forgive the phrase). A popular new variant is 'warming booby oil', marketed under the brand-name Hot Hooters. The most popular flavour is passion fruit.

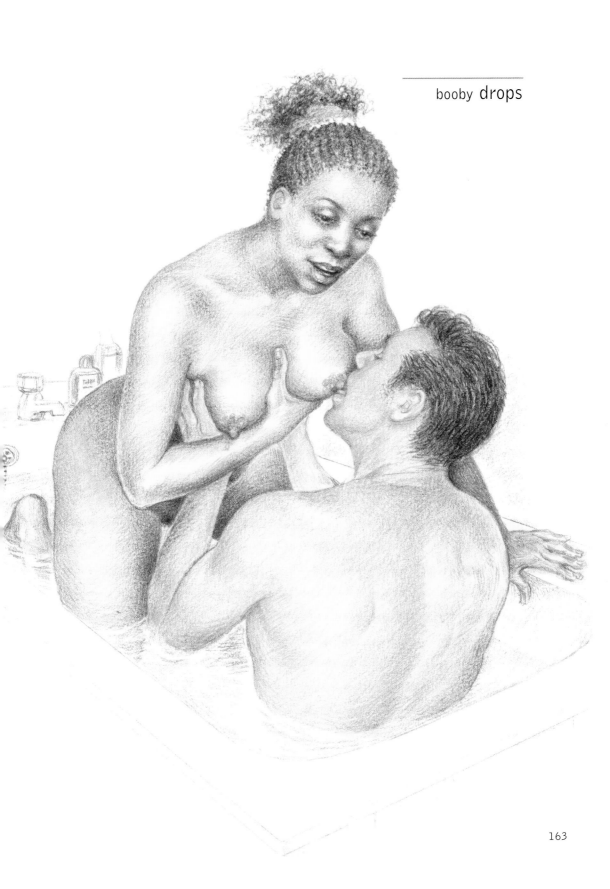

booby **drops**

All good fun: the booby drops are made in various fruity flavours such as orange and raspberry. And in some countries they have a variety which tastes of LAGER.

On second thoughts, I *am* now clear about which sex this particular aid is supposed to give most pleasure to…

GEISHA BALLS

Geisha balls – which are also known as 'duo-balls' – are shown in the drawing on this page.

I believe that they really were invented in Japan, where women are said to have a long tradition of pleasuring themselves with them.

What are they? Well, they are as you see – two little plastic balls connected by a thin string with a loop on the end. But inside each ball is a simple mechanism which makes the little sphere MOVE slightly if it's subjected to even the most minute pressure.

So, if the two balls are placed in the vagina, then they will respond to any shift in the woman's position by rolling around a little bit. This produces very pleasing feelings.

geisha balls

I know this may seem improbable, but there are women who wander round all day with geisha balls in their vaginas and – presumably – happy smiles on their faces. Certainly, I once knew an American sex therapist who used to travel across New York with these twin orbs rolling about inside her. Much to my surprise, she said that sometimes the stimulation was so great that she had to stop and masturbate. I suppose *anything's* possible in New York.

The only slight drawback of this device is that some brands tend to make quite a lot of noise as they bash against each other. If a woman really did decide to 'wear' them to the office, she could well give out an odd clonking sound as she moved around. Still, she could always say to her colleagues: 'Don't worry, it's only my balls banging together.'

To return to sex play… If your partner is interested in this device, then buy yourselves a pair and (when the moment is ripe) slip them gently into the opening of her vagina as shown in our drawing. You can put them right inside if that's what she fancies – or they can rest just inside the orifice, so they widen her S-for-stretch zone. Any movement she makes will now give her some interesting and pleasant sensations.

If you wish, you can leave the geisha balls inside her for a spell, while you do other nice things to her with your hands and mouth. Indeed, you can put your fingers inside at the same time as the balls if that's what takes her fancy.

And – although this book isn't about intercourse – some couples do like to actually make love with the duo-balls in the vagina. This seems to be quite helpful in cases where the woman's pelvic floor has grown slack through child-bearing, because the balls make things very snug. It's also claimed that using the balls can help a lady improve the tone of her vaginal muscles.

After the geisha balls have been in the vagina, you should take them out by slowly drawing the string downwards. Wash them thoroughly and then dry them.

Warning: never leave geisha balls or anything else inside the vagina for more than about six hours. Foreign bodies left in this delicate area can cause a discharge.

THE DILDO

A dildo is, of course, an artificial penis. For centuries dildos were made out of carved and painted wood, but these days they're more likely to be manufactured from plastic or latex.

I don't honestly think that the majority of couples are interested in them, but the fact that there has been a slow but steady demand for them over a period of at least three centuries (some poor soul was arrested in 1670 for trying to smuggle 350 of them into England) does rather indicate that they're useful to a lot of people.

In particular, I believe that they're a real help in some relationships where the man is no longer able to make love to the woman because of permanent impotence or illness.

Other couples just use them for a bit of fun; the man lubricates the dildo and then – as shown in the drawing below – slips it into his partner's vagina. If you try this, please resist the temptation (so ingrained in males) to ram it in hard. Just slip it in and out, and also use it lovingly to dilate the S-for-stretch zone.

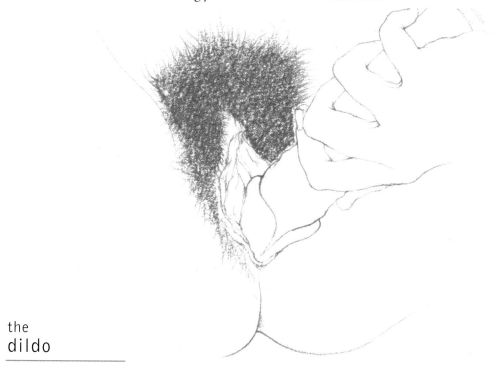

the
dildo

Some dildos are astoundingly realistic these days, and are made with 'veins' and moveable skin. Some have life-like testicles attached. Black ones are popular with white couples who want to fantasise about inter-racial sex... A few are 'double-ended' – for people whose love-lives somehow involve two bottoms.

PUBIC SHAMPOO

Pubic shampoo sells well in the sex shops, and I must say that the basic idea (shown in the drawing here) is very nice: in the shower or elsewhere, the guy pours some of this fragrant and pleasant-feeling stuff into his hands – and then gives his partner an agreeable shampoo of her pubes.

In fact, of course, you could perfectly well do this with any shampoo which you happen to have in the house! As the shampooing process continues, your partner may well (to borrow the words of the great John Donne):

pubic
shampoo

'Licence my
   roving hands
   and let them goe,
Behind, before, above, between,
   below.'

167

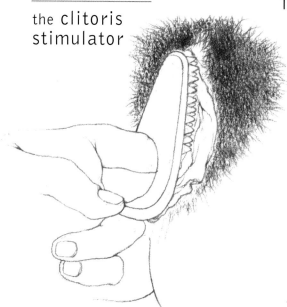

the **clitoris** stimulator

THE CLITORAL STIMULATOR

A clitoral stimulator is a little latex ring with, as you can see from the drawing here, a lot of small projections on it.

The stimulator is mostly used during intercourse; the man wears one round the base of his penis, so that (with luck) the bumpy bits rub against the woman's clitoris.

But you can also try using one during sex play. Just slip it over your thumb, or over two of your fingers, and then advance the fingertips into your partner's vagina, trying to ensure that the bobbles are rubbing on her clitoris.

Not easy, but it may be worth the attempt.

DON'T TOUCH SPANISH FLY!

Finally, a warning about an ALLEGED female sex aid – Spanish fly. Please have nothing whatever to do with this stuff.

Spanish fly is an extract of a squashed insect (the cantharides beetle). For centuries it's had a worldwide reputation as something which turns women on, if given by mouth. Unfortunately, this is nonsense – and dangerous nonsense.

What Spanish fly actually does is to create an inflammation in the urinary passages. In the old days, men apparently thought that causing such an irritation in this area would make a woman more raunchy. Strange idea!

But it's not just that Spanish fly is useless – it's potentially lethal. *The inflammation of the woman's urinary passages could kill her.*

I well remember a case in which a stupid young man put Spanish fly on snacks which he gave to two young women in his office, in the hope of seducing them. It killed them both.

Many sex shops sell tablets which they describe as 'Spanish fly'. The odds are that these contain nothing but sugar and flavouring.

10

OTHER SEX AID TECHNIQUES FOR A WOMAN TO USE ON A MAN

how a woman can use sex
aids to improve her man's
potency
cock feathers
the cock cage
the arab strap
other male supports
using oil in a sexy massage

HOW A WOMAN CAN USE SEX AIDS TO IMPROVE HER MAN'S POTENCY

I can't say that the sex aids a woman can use on a man are exactly the greatest thing since sliced bread, but a few of them are quite good fun.

Also – and I think this is very important – anything which can give a chap help with his erection can't be bad! I'm quite serious about this; both my wife (who is an Agony Aunt) and I receive dozens of letters each week from men who are having some trouble in getting it up.

Obviously, in really serious cases a guy with potency problems needs to be seen at a clinic which specializes in treating impotence. The drugs which are used to treat this condition are described at the end of this chapter.

But where the problem is relatively mild, some of the slightly wacky things described in this chapter may well help.

COCK FEATHERS

Cock feathers were (for some reason which now escapes me) first popularized by Bette Midler while on a promotional tour for one of her films.

You don't have to go to a sex shop to buy them: just get yourself an old-fashioned feather duster, as shown in the drawing. Then chase your man round the bedroom with it, tickling his apparatus whenever you can. A nice tickle with the feathers is great for getting blood into the penis.

So now you know why in England a feather duster is known as 'a tickling stick'.

cock
feathers

170

THE TEASER

This is one of several types of device (often known as 'cock cages') which support and stimulate the male organ during erection. The Teaser is an oval-shaped device which fits round the base of the penis. During actual intercourse the front part presses against the woman's clitoris, and the back part against her anus.

THE ARAB STRAP

The Arab Strap is shown in the drawing here. It's made of leather, with metal buckles and rings. It may look like something worn by a passing carthorse, but apparently they swear by it in the Middle East as an aid to erection. There are many different designs.

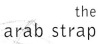

the
arab strap

Basically, all you have to do is to put it on your man – doing up any buckles – and generally jiggling it around a bit. The combination of friction and support is claimed to give him pleasure and help his erection.

I've a feeling that it's more likely to do this if he's a trifle into bondage or leather!

I believe that many couples then go on and have intercourse with the Arab Strap in situ. Personally, I'm not at all sure that this would be comfortable for the woman, but of course people vary greatly in their tastes.

Be careful about using the Arab Strap if either of you is allergic to metals, e.g. nickel.

OTHER MALE SUPPORTS

There's a wealth of other supporting devices which you can put on your man if you both fancy the idea.

All of them are based on much the same plan that constriction and friction around the penis will make blood flow into it and stay there. So in general, the idea is for you, to put them on lovingly and with a lot of verbal encouragement. And

SEX PLAY

once you've got them on, it's usually helpful if you stroke the bits of his penis which are (one hopes) bulging out through the gaps in the various devices.

One slightly different support is the Blakoe Energising Ring. This curious but popular British product has being going strong for many years. It's a black circlet which you put right round the base of your man's penis *and testicles*. It contains a couple of tiny metal plates which are supposed to generate a little electricity – and so aid him to get an erection. Personally I think it helps if his partner jogs it up and down a bit.

Although I can't support the manufacturers' enthusiastic claim for it as a great treatment for impotence, I think it's possible that it may give strength to some men's erections.

SEX PLAY, VIAGRA, AND OTHER DRUGS

If the man's having a bit of trouble with potency (that is, getting a good erection), it's perfectly OK to use Viagra – providing that a doctor has prescribed it. When Viagra first came out (in the USA) vast numbers of men who should never have been on it started using it – and the result was that several hundred of them died.

Even in the UK (where things are much more strictly controlled), about 100 males have died while on Viagra. But it's believed that most of these deaths were NOT related to the drug. Nonetheless, if you want to try the famous little blue diamond-shaped pills, you should get a check-up from a medic first.

Personally I've prescribed Viagra for well over 200 men – and in about 80% of them, it's been a great success. Minor side-effects (like headache and a flushed face) are common, but serious ones are rare.

In general, you need to take the Viagra tablet about ONE HOUR before sex play. It opens up the tubes which carry blood to your penis – and gives you a good, strong erection. But you do need penile stroking, kissing or sucking as well!

OTHER DRUGS Although it has had little publicity, the new drug Uprima (apomorphine) was introduced into the UK in the summer of 2001. You just put it under your tongue, and it works a great deal faster than Viagra; most men take it about 20 minutes before sex play. Again, you need to see a doctor before trying it, and you should read through the full list of side-effects, which is long.

Various other oral drugs are on the way. Injections and special pellets which you insert into the penis are also currently available, but are now nowhere near as popular as Viagra.

VIAGRA AND WOMEN At present, the manufacturers claim that in women, Viagra will not augment the pleasure of sex play. However there's some evidence that it may increase vaginal blood flow and sexual secretions (and, according to Italian researchers, sexual enjoyment and sex fantasies). Other drugs which certainly WILL turn women on are being developed.

USING OIL IN A SEXY MASSAGE

Now this is something that's really good. I do wish more couples went in for it as part of their sex play – especially as a preliminary. And it's not just something that a woman can use on her man; men can very successfully use it on women too. It's a wonderful way of easing the strains and pains of the day as you go into a sex play session. And as the massage proceeds, the two of you should gradually find it more and more erotic.

I'm going to describe it for a woman massaging a man, as we show in our illustration on page 175, but, as I say, the instructions will work equally well the other way round. Here goes:

- Buy yourself a bottle of some nice massage oil or cream. Sex shops sell brands with exotic-sounding names like 'Joy Jelly' and 'Emotion Lotion', but you can manage perfectly well with baby oil or anything of that type.
- However, bear in mind that if you're going to end up using a condom, its rubber will be damaged by certain products.
- Make sure the room is nice and warm and comfortable.
- Consider putting on some soft music.
- Both of you must be completely naked.
- Lie your partner flat on his face on the bed or couch, and kneel beside him.
- WARM some oil in your cupped hands (cold oil is very jarring), and then apply a little to his shoulders.
- It is over the back of the shoulders and in the neck that most people have

SEX PLAY

such a lot of tension these days. So start kneading the flesh over his shoulders with your oiled fingers, and then VERY gradually work over to his neck.

- When you get to his neck, use the tips of your fingers and thumbs to gently prod in between the bones which you can feel under the skin. If he says that a point hurts, then that's the place to keep working on with the oil!

- Now start *gradually* moving your hands down the upper part of his spine, in between his shoulder-blades. This is a place of terrific tension for many people, especially those with desk jobs.

- Push your thumb-tips in between the bones of his spine – paying special attention to any areas which are tender.

- In the same way, work down to his lower spine – and eventually to his buttocks. Don't go in between them unless you've read the hygiene advice in the next chapter.

- Now switch to his CALVES and gradually work up the backs of his legs till you get to his buttocks again. Throughout, use plenty of the oil.

- Then you turn him over, and start working on the FRONT of his shoulders – and his chest muscles. Don't forget to warm the oil in your hands before every fresh application.

- Finally, work your oiled hands down over his belly and into his pubic hair. What you do next is up to you…

an oil
massage

11

POSTILLIONAGE

(ANAL PLAY) TECHNIQUES FOR A MAN TO USE ON A WOMAN — AND THEIR RISKS

sex and bottoms
a vital hygiene warning
how to do postillionage
a horse in each stable
postillionage sex aids

SEX AND BOTTOMS

It's not surprising that many women have discovered that they enjoy having a lover's fingertip gently caress their anal regions during love-making, as shown in our illustration on these pages – or in the course of sex play. In a sex survey which I recently conducted among a large group of British women, 45 per cent said 'Yes, I've been stimulated in this way.' Half of them said that it turned them on, though some didn't like it – so it's clearly not for *every* woman by any means.

But there's no doubt that it helps some women reach orgasm. Others report that they get very intense climaxes from the extra kick of having the bottom stroked at the same time as the clitoris and/or vagina (see below, if you'll forgive the phrase).

Most of the couples who go in for postillionage don't seem to appreciate that there are definite HYGIENE risks involved if you don't take care about what you're doing. So *please* read the next section before you attempt any bottom play on your partner.

HYGIENE WARNING

The rectum – unlike the vagina – isn't a very clean area of the body. In other words, it normally contains germs. Some of these germs are harmless, but others could cause:

- Vaginal discharge.
- Urinary infection.
- Food poisoning and related ailments.

So, if a man is going to put his finger on or up his partner's bottom there are three hygiene precautions he should take:

- After the finger has touched her anus, he must NOT put it anywhere near her

giving her
postillionage

vagina, and especially her urinary opening

- As soon as possible after sex play is over, he should wash his finger.
- Please: *no* preparing of any nice after-sex snacks or drinks until the hand has been washed.

SHOULD THE WOMAN TAKE ANY HYGIENE PRECAUTIONS?

Well, if she asks her man to do this caress on her, it's reasonable for her to ensure that she has been to the loo some time during the previous hour or so – in order to try to make certain that her bottom is empty. Sorry to be so blunt, but it's clearly not a good idea hygiene-wise for a lover to be sticking his finger into bowel motions. It's also most unromantic…

Is there any risk of AIDS from postillionage? This is a reasonable question, since anal *intercourse* is of course a very efficient way of passing on the HIV virus. However, at the moment postillionage seems to be a low-risk activity, especially for couples who are totally faithful to each other.

RIMMING For the sake of completeness, I should add that there's an activity called 'rimming', in which the lover actually kisses or tongues the lady's bottom. I really would strongly advice *against* this, because even in apparently healthy couples it could pass on such germs as the hepatitis one.

HOW TO DO POSTILLIONAGE

Now if you're going to do it to your partner, here's how. First, *ensure she's agreeable.* Not all women want this done to them. Furthermore, please remember that many women do get sore bottoms from time to time – and as you'll readily appreciate, when your backside is sore, you're not terribly likely to want a chap to touch it up.

Assuming she wants you to go ahead, the next thing to consider is the question of lubrication. Although a lot of couples go in for postillionage with no lubrication at all, the fact is that the female anus is easily cut or split by pressure. So I would strongly urge you to put something creamy or oily on your index finger – even if it's only the butter which was popularized long ago in the Brando film *Last Tango in Paris*. Also, make very sure that your fingernail is trimmed and has no jagged edges.

No man in his right mind carries out postillionage on a woman *by itself*: this would be very unromantic and would almost certainly do nothing for her. So before you start, you need to be doing something else to her, such as stroking her breasts and/or clitoris with your other hand.

When you're sure she is fully relaxed and happy, all you need do is to run your fingertip around the opening. Given reasonable luck, this should increase the pleasure of whatever you're doing to her already. Indeed, in a woman who's already very near a climax, this additional stimulation will often tip her over the brink.

I really wouldn't recommend putting your finger *inside* unless the two of you are thoroughly used to each other's bodies and trust each other completely. Bear in mind that if she is nervous, she will tighten up and that will make it uncomfortable for her – in which case you must of course stop.

But in the case of two long-term lovers who understand each other fully and who take a pride in lovingly giving each other very intense sensations in bed, this kind of deep postillionage with your forefinger right inside her can give her the most enormous sense of fulfilment, especially if you are also using clitoris-stimulation to bring her to orgasm.

A HORSE IN EACH STABLE

This is an equestrian term which describes the common sex play practice of putting one finger inside a lady's bottom – while putting another finger inside her vagina.

Properly done, this gives her an agreeable sense of fullness and stretching. If you find some simple way of stimulating her clitoris at the same time (e.g. with your thumb or with a vibrator or by letting her do it), the result is often a very intense orgasm for her.

If you try this technique, I think that it's better to use *separate* hands (for instance, putting the index finger of your left hand in her bottom and one of the fingers of your right hand in her vagina) rather than using two fingers of the same hand – which could be unhygienic.

Incidentally, if you use the Horse in Each Stable method on your partner, you'll be able to feel that the partition between the vagina and the rectum is remarkably THIN. Once you've felt this, you will immediately realize how important it is to be *gentle* when putting anything into either of these delicate openings of her body.

SEX PLAY

POSTILLIONAGE SEX AIDS, INCLUDING THAI BEADS

As you'd expect, the intrepid manufacturers of sex aids have come up with many devices intended to help men perform what one might term mechanical postillionage on women. For all of them, you MUST follow the hygiene rules outlined on page 178 - 179.

There are many rectal vibrators which are specifically designed for this kind of thing. You must not use ORDINARY vaginal vibrators because, from time to time, they disappear up somebody's bottom, never to return. In those circumstances, the poor woman has to be taken into hospital with the thing buzzing away, deep inside her abdomen. Doctors call the appearance which is produced 'R.U.S.' – or 'Rotating Umbilicus Syndrome'.

Rectal vibrators have a sort of hilt (like a sword-hilt) which is supposed to prevent that kind of disaster. Most other rectal stimulation devices (like the famous butt plugs, which are intended simply to give a pleasant feeling of fullness in the bottom area) have similar safety features.

That's certainly true of the world-famous Thai beads, which are shown in the drawing on the opposite page. I have to be utterly frank with you and confess that I wouldn't like to be on the receiving end of this, but they're very popular in Old Siam, and apparently find a ready market with couples all over the globe.

They're usually made of black latex, and the general idea is that during sex play; the man slowly inserts the string of four lubricated beads into the woman's bottom. The butterfly-shaped handle makes sure they can't disappear inside her. (At least, not unless the string breaks.)

And what's the point of them? Well, at the moment of her climax – which would usually be induced by clitoris-stimulation – the man suddenly whips them out… Whoops!

There are women who speak highly of this slightly bizarre practice. But I definitely don't think you should attempt it if your partner is suffering from any minor bottom problems, such as piles.

thai
beads

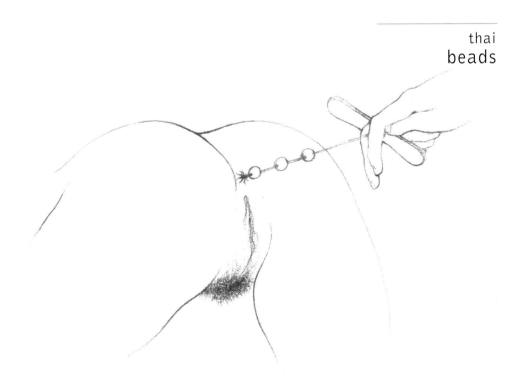

12

POSTILLIONAGE

(ANAL PLAY) TECHNIQUES FOR A WOMAN TO USE ON A MAN

a few basic facts
hygiene precautions
what to do
massaging his prostate
sex aids and his bottom

A FEW BASIC FACTS

In one of my recent surveys, almost four out of ten women said that they'd touched up their men's bottoms during sex play It's also often done during intercourse, in the way shown on pages 190 - 191.

But a lot of women DON'T like doing it – 53 per cent in my survey – and if that applies to you, then my advice is: don't let yourself be forced into it. It's certainly not an essential part of sex play. However, if you do go in for it, you ought to be aware of four basic facts:

- It's NORMAL for there to be erotic nerve-endings in a bloke's bottom (the same is true of women's bottoms).
- So the fact that your man may ask you to touch him up doesn't mean that he's gay!
- Touching him there may well help him to have an erection – or indeed to have a climax.
- If you do touch his bottom, you MUST take certain hygiene precautions – see the next section.

HYGIENE PRECAUTIONS

These are the safety measures you must take, for your own protection as well as his:

- After you've touched him up, don't touch anything else with that finger till it's been washed.
- In particular, don't let that finger go anywhere near your clitoris, vagina or U-spot.
- And don't touch any food with it.

In addition (as you'll know if you read the previous chapter), it's important that the *recipient* of this particular caress should take care that his bottom is clean – and empty.

WHAT TO DO

If you're sure that you're happy to go ahead, here's what you do.

Lubricate your finger with baby oil, face cream, Vaseline or whatever, and slip it between his buttocks. Now run the fingertip gently round in circles, so that you caress his opening. That's Stage One.

Bear in mind that many men find this simple movement very exciting. So take care you don't tip him over into orgasm without meaning to. (It's not a great idea to use this caress on premature ejaculators…).

Stage Two is to ease your fingertip inside. This is quite easy, provided you've used that lubricant. Most women then make a sort of in-and-out motion with the finger – though in practice, the movement you can make may be slightly limited, depending on what else you're doing at the time.

You could, for instance, be simultaneously giving him oral sex, or receiving it from him, or giving or receiving hand-petting – or having intercourse. In some of these situations it can be quite difficult for a woman to reach all the way round her man's buttocks and waggle her finger without getting cramp. Especially if she has short arms.

MASSAGING HIS PROSTATE

Perhaps the most exotic version of postillionage is this one, which you may perhaps have read about in Harold Robbins novels (no plot, but plenty of prostate…). The prostate, by the way, is said by many to be the equivalent of a woman's G-spot.

The general idea here is that when your finger is inside his bottom – as shown in the drawing here shows – you use the fingertip to stroke his prostate gland, which is a part of his reproductive apparatus that can only be reached by this route. It's basically the same thing that doctors do when they examine a chap's prostate, but with *you* doing it, it should be a lot more enjoyable. Slip your lubricated index finger well inside, with the pad of the finger upwards, as shown. A couple of inches (about 5 cm) in, you'll find that there's something bulging under your fingerpad. That's his prostate.

It's usually about the size of a horse-chestnut, but may be

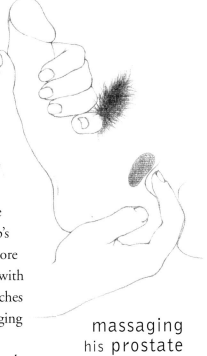

massaging
his **prostate**

quite a bit bigger, especially if your man is over forty. Be prepared for the fact that, unless you're used to this sort of thing, it may take you a while to identify it with confidence.

But once you've found it, stroke it. Your man should immediately get an unusual feeling of pleasure – which, once again, some people claim is similar to the rather exotic sensation which many women experience when the G-spot is stroked.

The prostate gland produces part of your man's seminal fluid. So it's not surprising that after you've been stroking it for a minute or two, a drop or two of clear liquid from his prostate will appear at the tip of his penis. (This fluid doesn't have any particular taste or smell; it may contain sperms.)

The appearance of the dewdrop at the tip of his cock doesn't necessarily mean that he's about to reach a climax, but it does mean that he's fairly excited. However, it will probably require actual rubbing of his penis to make him come.

Whether you go on massaging his prostate up until the moment of orgasm is up to you – and him. But if you do so, he will probably have quite an intense orgasm, especially if you happen to touch the tiny organs next to the prostate (the seminal vesicles).

Very strikingly, in younger men the prostatic massage will often make the seminal fluid shoot out an extraordinary distance when the climax occurs. I'm not exaggerating when I say that it can occasionally wind up on top of your heads. The volume is often increased too.

Incidentally, this prostatic massage is worth bearing in mind if you suffer from fertility problems. When the guy's sperm count is on the low side, using your finger to coax a little extra spunk from him could be just the job. Or even just the hand-job.

I need scarcely say that massaging round the prostate is a great idea if your man sometimes has erection problems. It's difficult *not* to have an erection when the woman you love is giving you the 'treatment' illustrated in our drawing on page 187.

SEX AIDS AND HIS BOTTOM

As I explained in the last chapter, you mustn't put anything inside the rectum which could get lost up there. There are special rectal vibrators which are designed to prevent this happening.

You can also use the famous Thai beads (see previous chapter) on your man – if he's feeling brave. And sex shops do sell things called 'butt plugs' which some guys like pushed in a short distance during sex play or intercourse. They are also designed so they won't vanish into his rectum.

Are there are sex aids for the prostate? Well, there is the celebrated Chinese Prostate Violin! This is a very, very slim one-stringed fiddle which oriental courtesans used to slip into their clients' bottoms. The end of the device is intended to rest against the prostate, and as the courtesan draws her bow across the instrument's string, the fair melodies which she produces are supposed to resound magnificently throughout the innermost recesses of his sexual apparatus.

Hence, no doubt, the phrase 'There's many a good tune played on an old fiddle'…

SEX PLAY

giving him
postillionage

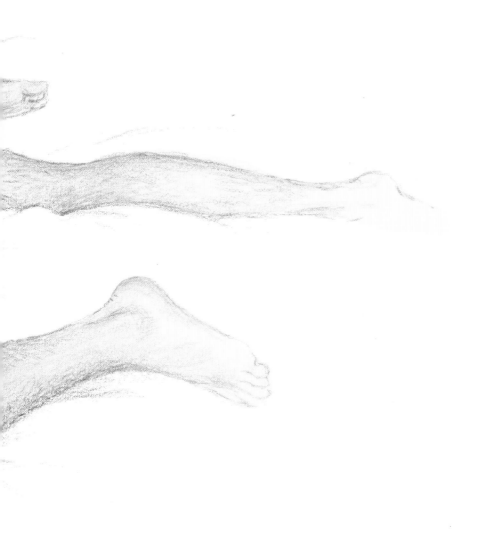

BREAST
PLAY

BREASTS, SEXUAL AROUSAL AND ORGASM

One of the great things about sex play involving the woman's breasts is that it gives such immense pleasure and satisfaction to *both* parties. Men are mostly obsessed with the beautiful female mammary, and just adore looking at it, squeezing it and stroking it; similarly, most women love having their breasts admired – and delight in having them caressed and kissed. (This is true of lesbians as well as heterosexual females.)

Incidentally, I have found that if a woman loses this great joy in her breasts, it is often due to some serious psychological crisis *involving her child*. Thus, I once saw a patient who complained of a total loss of nipple and mammary sexual sensation – immediately after she'd discovered that her daughter was a drug addict. When the daughter's condition eventually improved, the mother found that she could once again derive sexual pleasure from her breasts.

As you'd imagine, the boobs have very strong nerve connections with the emotional and pleasure centres of a woman's brain. That's why sexual arousal and orgasm produce very striking changes in the skin of the breast and in the nipple (changes first documented during various extraordinary experiments by the US sex researchers Masters and Johnson, who somehow persuaded a lot of women to have climaxes in the laboratory while their heaving bosoms were being filmed in close up…)

The main changes that you will notice during sex play are that as a lady becomes more and more interested, her boobs get very slightly bigger, while her nipples become prominent – this actually makes them a bit more accessible to the techniques we're going to run through in this chapter. By the way, smaller breasts react in exactly the same way as bigger ones – and are just as erotically sensitive.

Does stimulation of the breasts produce orgasm? I often get letters from people who are worried about this. ('My wife and I understand that she *ought* to be able to come as a result of nipple stimulation alone…')

However, the honest fact is that most women can't be brought to orgasm by breast stimulation without any clitoral or vaginal friction. It's true that there are some females who can do it just through having their nipples stroked – in a recent study of 'easily orgasmic women', the American scientists found that no less than 20 per cent of their group could manage it. Lucky them! But a less dramatic figure for the general population was produced by the above-mentioned Masters and Johnson – who studied 4000 orgasms and found that only THREE out of their group of women could do it. Admittedly, this was at a time (the 1960s and 1970s) when many females were still very uptight, sexually.

Perhaps the most important thing to say about breast play is that far too often it's neglected. Again and again over the years, I've had wives complain to me that 'my husband never strokes my boobs these days'. So, men: do your duty!

Finally, just a note about MEN and their nipples. Not all women realize that most blokes are capable of deriving very nice sensations from the erotic nerve-endings in the nipples. Therefore, don't hesitate to try out the techniques mentioned below on your guy. Sucking and licking are very effective on males.

MOUTH PLAY

Using your mouth to stimulate your partner's nipples is tremendously erotic. But a word of warning: do take it a bit gently; the breast is a delicate organ, and you can easily cause pain instead of pleasure if you're a bit too enthusiastic with sucking, or with use of your teeth.

In fact, I personally wouldn't recommend using your incisors on a woman's breast at all, though there's no doubt that some females do like to have the nipple taken tenderly between the man's teeth. If you do this, sir, do it with care.

Love bites on the breast itself (as opposed to the nipple) are OK – provided that the lady is agreeable. Sorry to keep quoting my own surveys, but in a recent one I was surprised to find that a very substantial minority of women disliked being love-bitten anywhere – and particularly on the breast.

What about sucking? Well, this simple technique – illustrated in the drawing on page 196 and 197 – often works wonders in bed. Don't be shy about it: put your mouth over her areola (that's the darkish disc which surrounds her nipple) and draw the nipple itself firmly but lovingly into your mouth.

You can actually draw it out to quite a length – a couple of inches (about 5 cm) or so in many women. Be guided by her reaction as to how hard you should suck, and how far you should draw it out. And while it's in your mouth, don't hesitate to tickle and tease it with your tongue.

Next, of course, there's licking – which is shown in the drawing on page 198.

SEX PLAY

Here, the main trick is to use a *moist* tongue-tip. If you keep everything nice and wet as you draw the tip of your tongue across her nipple and areola, you won't go far wrong. Try to tickle, tease and titillate her – in fact, titillate is a word that might have been designed for the breasts, don't you think?

HAND PLAY

It seems to be part of human nature to want to take the breasts in one's two hands and squeeze them. Indeed, many passionate women will actually do this to themselves during sexual excitement. If you're a man, you can actually help your partner to reach orgasm during intercourse or sex play by cupping her boobs in your hands and squeezing them – if more guys bore this simple fact in mind, there would be less problems with failure to climax.

What else can you do with your hands? Well, don't forget to STROKE your partner's breasts – another thing that's often neglected. And I'd strongly recommend the technique shown in our drawing on page 201, in which you just take your lover's nipple between finger and thumb, and then:

- Roll it.
- Squeeze it.
- Draw it out.

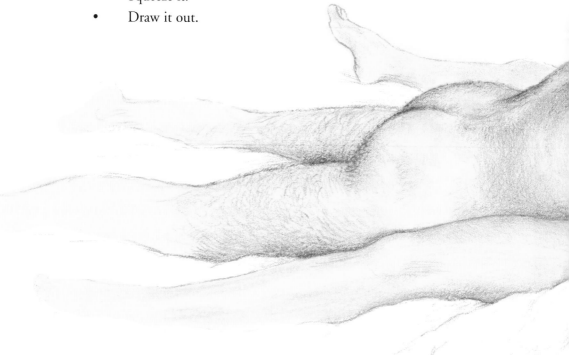

Provided your partner likes this kind of thing, you can actually draw the nipple out quite a long way from the breast. I have known women who are stimulating themselves to pull the nipple out several inches, and then let it twang back again. Happily, the nipple is usually a very elastic structure.

OTHER METHODS OF STIMULATING HER BREASTS

There are also some rather more way-out methods of stimulating the breasts. Many women find that the gentle application of a vibrator to the nipple is quite pleasant – though it certainly isn't as effective in this part of the body as it is elsewhere. I have not so far come across any specially-designed breast vibrator – but after reading this, no doubt someone will invent one!

Stroking your partner's boobs with certain sensuous materials often works very well: velvet is very good, and so are the fur gloves popularized by James Bond and the sexy physiotherapist in

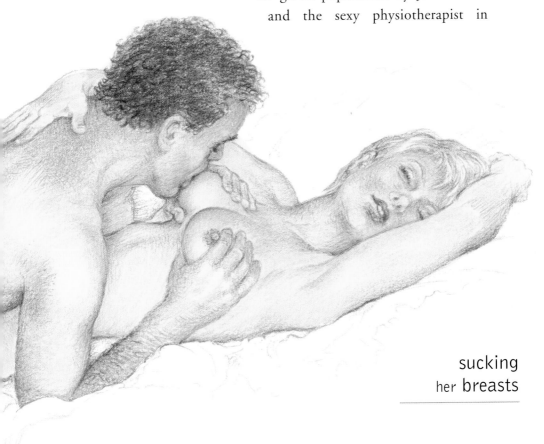

sucking
her breasts

Thunderball. These days, they'd better be *fake* fur – the days of mink gloves should be over.

If your partner is into leather, then doubtless stroking her tits with a white or brown driving glove would be exciting for her, but I'm afraid I have done no research in this particular area.

Ice is sometimes used on the nipples by exotically-minded couples. But only do it if the lady is totally happy about it. And clearly, the ice must NOT be cold enough to cause her any pain. Incidentally, ice and snow (brrr – rr!) have been used for centuries by women to promote nipple erection – and it's said that topless models still sometimes use ice-cubes for this purpose.

Also, don't

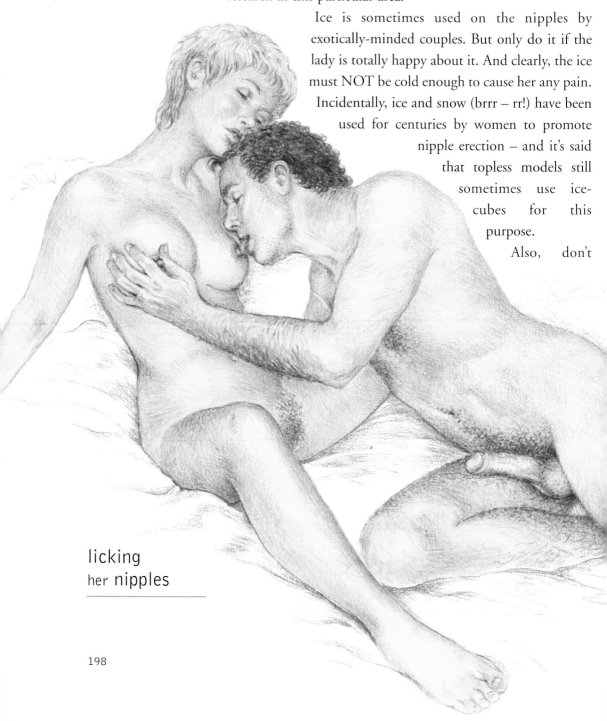

licking
her nipples

198

forget the tremendous importance of soap and warm water on the breasts. Many women really adore having their boobs lovingly lathered by a partner, whether in the shower or the bath or elsewhere. Putting on the lather with a nice soft flannel or sponge often adds to the fun, but you can do it perfectly well with your palms and fingertips.

HEALTH NOTE Feeling the breasts with a soapy hand is a *very* good way of detecting lumps. If, sir, you ever notice an apparent lump in your partner's breast during sex play, I beg you to encourage her to see a doctor and have it checked out within 48 hours. This advice could be life-saving.

BREASTS AND THE PENIS

Finally, let's not forget that sexy couples have always found that games involving the penis and the breasts are an enjoyable part of sex play.

So, here are some good things for you to try out:

- Rub the tip of your man's erect penis against your nipple – and watch your nipple stand out in response. Quite a lot of women like it if the penis then delivers a small dewdrop of 'tribute' on to the breast.
  - Kneel forward so that your boobs dangle gracefully, and then let your nipples sweep across his shaft and head.
    - If your breasts are fairly big, you'll find it quite easy to put his cock between them so that you squeeze it from either side. This works best if you're lying on top of him.
    - Even if your boobs are quite small, you can put his penis between them and hold it there with your hand. Then, if you like, you can vigorously stimulate him with your fingers.

S E X   P L A Y

• You can try The Bagpiper, which is shown in our drawing below. The expression 'bagpiping' means putting his erect cock between your breasts, and then dipping your head forward to as to suck the head of his penis. The resemblance to the noble musical instrument of Scotland is obvious…

Whether you let him go all the way and actually come during breast-penis play is up to you. But this is something that many guys certainly do appreciate once in a while.

bagpiping

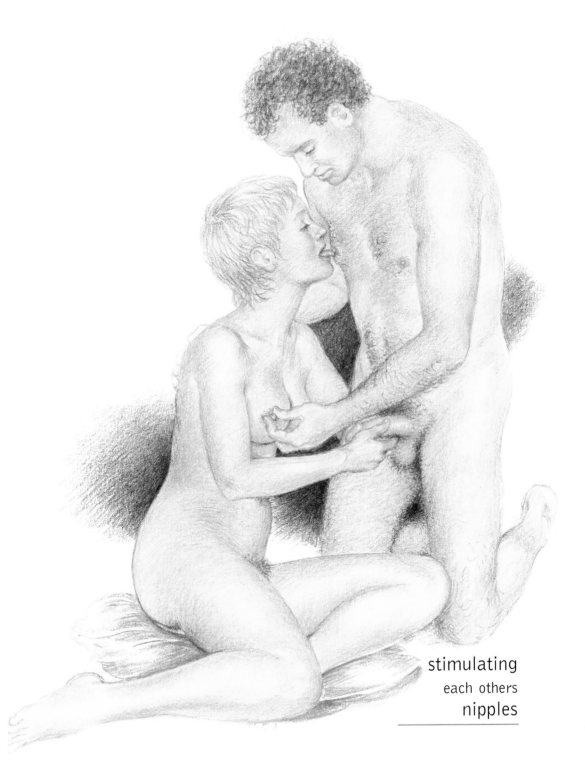

stimulating
each others
nipples

LAUGHTER AND

BEDTIME

GAMES

THE VALUE OF LAUGHTER IN BED

Do you laugh together a lot in bed? I do hope so, because laughter really is a great tonic where sex is concerned.

You see, far too many people take sex play much too seriously. They treat it like an Olympic event, or like a game of chess. They write to me and say things like:

> Dear Dr Delvin,
> Last night I pressed my wife's clitoris for the first time ever, but nothing happened. I am sure this means she must be abnormal…

Ye gods! This is treating a woman like a computer. If you want your sex life together to be a success, then don't take that sort of mechanistic and deadly serious attitude.

Instead, try to see the *funny* side of sex together – especially when things go wrong (as they invariably will sometimes). Play lots of amusing bedtime games with each other, and when you're touching each other up, make sure you have time for a tickle and a giggle. For laughing together is a precious gift – more precious than a million climaxes.

FANTASIES

As part of your sex play, fantasies are fine – especially if they happen to be wacky fantasies that make you both chuckle a bit.

But don't get yourselves into anything heavy, and above all please avoid any fantasy which might cause distress to your partner. For instance, it's a well-known fact – confirmed by survey after survey – that the secret personal fantasies which many men and women drift into during sex *involve thoughts about other people.* During intercourse, 56 per cent of females sometimes fantasize about having sex with some other guy. And in 2001 we did an internet survey that found that 40% of female respondents fantasized about lesbianism.

I honestly do not think you should tell your partner about that kind of personal fantasy unless you're really sure that he/she can cope with it and wouldn't be hurt.

But I reckon that there's a lot to be said for mutual – and totally harmless – fantasies during sex play For instance:

- He's a Roman soldier and she's a vestal virgin.
- He's a totally inexperienced teenager, and she's a worldly-wise older woman who's going to initiate him into sex play.
- She's the posh lady of the manor, and he is but a humble manservant whom she's allowed into her bedroom. You can see the general idea in the drawing on page 206.
- One of you belongs to some other race or nationality. ('*Ciao*! I am this very sexy Italian guy…') If you already ARE Italian, then be a kilted Scotsman or a love-hungry Zulu or something).
- She's a policewoman who's just arrested him for speeding – but she's willing to let him go in return for certain services.
- They're not really in their bedroom, and instead they're touching each other up in some outrageous place – like a Mediterranean nudist beach, or the front row of the Metropolitan Opera.

As long as you're both happy with a sex play fantasy, then the sky's the limit. But two brief warnings:

- Don't let yourself become obsessed with a particular fantasy. Psychologists have found that there's a curious tendency for men and women to get hooked on certain fantasies, if they keep using them again and again. This addiction to one special fantasy is liable to occur if you make a habit of always thinking about it just before you climax – because that's a time when your mind is very vulnerable to being imprinted with ideas. For instance, if a woman keeps thinking about a particular film star just before she comes, she may well reach a stage when she can't reach orgasm at all without fantasizing about him.
- Don't be daft enough to try to put your fantasies INTO REALITY. This can be disastrous. The commonest example of this is the situation where a husband and wife like to pretend that Mr and Mrs Jones from down the road are getting involved in their sex play with them. Then they make the fatal mistake of inviting Mr and Mrs Jones to pop round and engage *in the real thing*… Not wise at all.

SEX PLAY

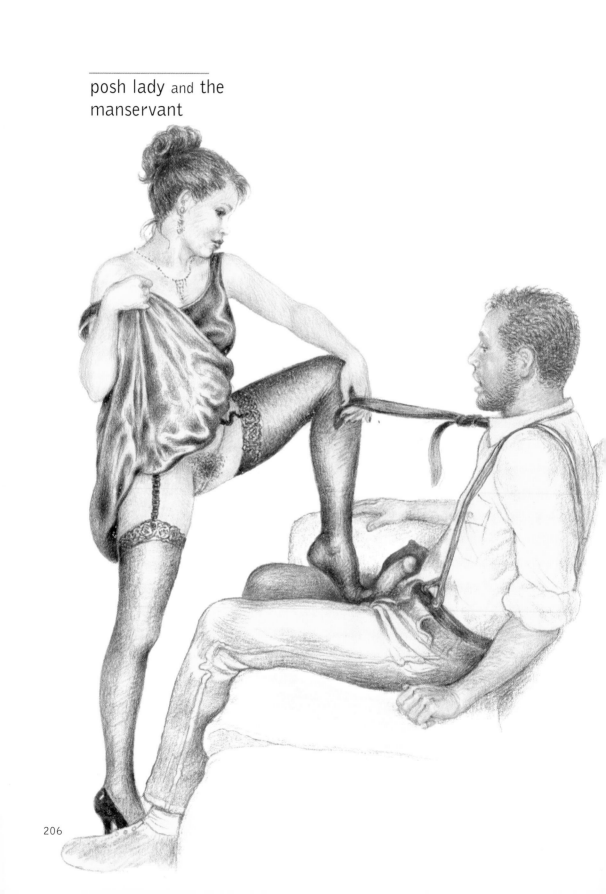

DRESSING UP FOR SEX

When a couple have been together for quite a while and want to put a bit more spice into their sex play, a little dressing up can be just the thing. Obviously, I'm not suggesting that this is worth bothering about if you're a pair of young lovers who are *desperate* for each other's bodies, and who just want to eat each other and screw each other all evening

But if your relationship is a few years old, then a quick dip into the dressing-up box can be a useful way of ensuring a frivolous and fun-filled session of sex play. And you don't need any complicated or hard-to-find costumes either. In many cases, a couple of old-fashioned hats plus some scarves will be enough to give you a wacky but effective disguise.

Here are some ideas:

BASQUE AND MASK Imagine you're both going to a masked ball – and in a way, you are… She dresses up in a basque as in our illustration on page 208, and both of you hide your faces behind masks. A few couples actually prefer the chance to wear the basque; whatever turns you on. Put on some nice ballroom-type music – maybe Johann Strauss – and dance around exchanging compliments and caresses till you finally reveal yourselves.

COWBOYS AND INDIANS Discreetly borrow a Western hat and a few feathers from the kids. Embellish with anything else that takes your fancy – such as spurs, bows and arrows or a toy gun (a vibrator would make a useful substitute). Now chase each other round the bedroom, pausing from time to time to try various techniques outlined in this book…

WINTER WOOLIES Pretend it's a freezing cold day, and dress up in all kinds of warm winter clothes – but only on your head, hands and feet. Sex play with someone who's wearing nothing but a furry hat, woollen gloves and Wellington boots can be an interesting experience…

DOCTORS AND NURSES For obvious professional reasons, I'd never play this game myself. But it is popular with a lot of couples. Borrow a pair of white coats

SEX PLAY

basque and
mask

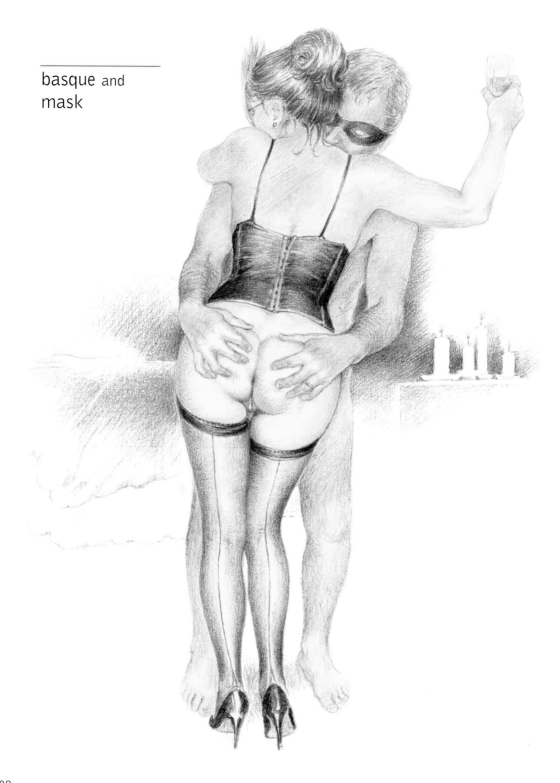

or a starched apron and a cap, and you're in business. Examine each other thoroughly, not forgetting the intimate places.

BONDAGE GAMES

Though they're definitely not for everybody, gentle tying-up games are relished by a substantial minority of couples. In my survey of over 6000 women, one in five had tried this sort of thing – and a little over half of those said they liked it. However, bondage is definitely MUCH more popular with men – as the massive male sales of movies about 'tied-up sex' will testify!

If you want to make it part of your sex play, PLEASE follow these rules:

- Use only soft things for tying each other up: velvet bands or the belts of towelling dressing-gowns are OK. Hard ropes, cords or string are NOT.
- For heaven's sake, keep your 'bonds' away from your partner's neck and face. Every year, tragedies occur because some fool has decided to tie a ligature round the throat area.
- Have nothing to do with gags. These too can kill people.
- Before you start, agree on a password which means 'You must release me at once.'

How you play mild bondage games is up to you and your partner. But not a bad plan is for one of you to tie the other one's wrists and ankles to the bedposts – then tease, tickle and stroke his/her defenceless body into ecstasy.

SMACKS AND WHATNOT

Sorry to disappoint those of you who are heavily into sado-masochism, but I'm afraid that I am most certainly NOT going to recommend the infliction of real pain in bed.

Still, it's a well-known psychological fact that loving couples often do get turned on by exchanging tiny amounts of pain during sex play. Thus, in the above-mentioned survey of over 6000 women, I found that 15 per cent of them liked a little bit of bottom spanking – and a very few could actually reach orgasm this way (invariably when they were on the receiving end, so to speak).

SEX PLAY

209

But if you both agree that you're going to do it to each other, I do suggest that you keep it gentle. Often, a more effective technique for a man to use is simply to pinch or *squeeze* his partner's buttocks firmly during sexual stimulation: this often heightens her excitement quite a bit.

A similar word of caution about causing pain with love bites. In my survey, only 36 per cent of women actually liked receiving love bites – which men are, of course, very keen on dishing out. Think carefully, guys, and make sure that your partner doesn't mind this kind of thing.

VISUAL HELP: MIRRORS, VIDEOS AND EROTICA

For over 25 years now, both British and American sex therapists have used visual aids to stimulate people's sex drive. It's a fact that for many couples (though certainly not all) looking at sexy images can be a turn-on.

But it's worth noting that women in particular *have to be in the right mood for this sort of thing*. A female can be excited by an erotic image one night, and then find that on the following evening she's bored by it or even repelled by it.

So what sort of images could enhance your sex play? Well, here are some of the most popular ideas:

MIRRORS Many couples find that seeing themselves in mirrors while they're going in for sex play is thrilling. Of course, it's not *quite* so thrilling if either of you is out of shape or has a pot belly. However, if you're both in reasonable condition, then a strategically-placed mirror or two can certainly be a help – especially during love manoeuvres like the 69, in which you really couldn't see very much of the other person without the aid of a looking glass.

VIDEOS OF YOURSELF Since home videos became available, many couples have started discreetly using them as aids to sex play For instance, one partner may video the other one having a climax – and then play it back during a later sex session. Just be careful that you keep these home movies where the kids can't find them!

COMMERCIAL VIDEOS OR DVD'S By the early years of the 21st century,

HUGE numbers of couples had started using erotic videos in their sex play. Many hotel chains offer them, and vast numbers are sold in shops and by mail order. A few tips:

- Make sure you pick a video which your partner actually LIKES!
- Position the video-player/TV screen where both of you can easily see it from the bed.
- Remember that one or both of you may need your glasses by the bedside in order to see the finer points…
- Having the remote control by the bed may be helpful if you want to replay something that your partner found very erotic.

THE EROTIC PRINT SOCIETY AND THE EROTIC REVIEW And of course, my publishers, The Erotic Print Society and their magazine, The Erotic Review, publish a wealth of erotica, both photographic and artistic, contemporary and historic, non-fiction and fiction. Erotica is more sophisticated than pornography, but often just as explicit; it usually targets the brain rather than the groin, and is more artistic than exploitative: for this reason it's often easier for couples to share, discuss and enjoy together. Details about 'EPS' and 'ER' are available at the end of the book.

SUMMING UP

So there you are, dear readers: this is the end of my book on how to make sex play FUN. Hope you've enjoyed it.

I leave you with a couple of thoughts, which are mainly directed at male readers:

- My researches indicate that the average bloke still thinks that sex play need only last for a few minutes; but the average woman would like it to last up to half an hour – and maybe a lot more!
- Although there's been some improvement in male sex play skills over recent years, most women still don't rate us guys all that highly in this department. For instance, when I told a well-known broadcaster

that I was just finishing a book on sex play, she remarked grimly:

'What's the difference between a pub and a clitoris? Let me tell you, doctor: *A man can always find a pub.*'

So try hard, male readers, won't you? The honour of our sex is at stake!

Finally, can I offer you an optimistic slogan for those who are trying to keep long-term relationships going, in these difficult and dangerous times:

THE COUPLE WHO PLAY TOGETHER ... STAY TOGETHER.

Let's hope so, anyway. *Ave atque vale*, as Ovid himself might have said.

after sex
play

INDEX

Yates Garden Guide

The *Yates Garden Guide* has been the gardening bible for New Zealanders since 1895 and this revised, updated edition ensures that New Zealand's gardeners will stay in touch with today's gardening trends and products.

This seventy-sixth edition combines more than one hundred years of gardening experience with fresh insights and up-to-date advice on all aspects of gardening. New to this edition is information on growing plants in difficult conditions: coastal gardens, shady areas, clay soils, very dry or very wet conditions, and courtyard gardens. Also featured is a chapter on today's special plants: bromeliads, succulents, cacti, proteas, ornamental grasses and foliage plants. Colour photographs throughout and helpful step-by-step diagrams, plus tips from the experts, make this the must-have guide for all gardeners.

HarperCollins*Publishers*